Drug Addiction: Crime or Disease?

DRUG ADDICTION: CRIME OR DISEASE?

Interim *and* Final Reports *of the* Joint
Committee of the American Bar Association
and the American Medical Association
on Narcotic Drugs

Introduction by
ALFRED R. LINDESMITH

Indiana University Press
Bloomington

FOURTH PRINTING 1963

Introduction copyright © 1961 by Indiana University Press

Manufactured in the United States of America

Library of Congress catalog card number: 61-9838

CONTENTS

INTRODUCTION

The work of the Joint Committee of the American Bar Association and the American Medical Association on Narcotic Drugs may well be a landmark in the history of the drug problem in this country. It marks the first cooperative undertaking between these two important professions in this area in which both are vitally involved and in which both have important practical responsibilities. It is safe to say that if and when basic changes are made in present methods of handling the drug problem these two professions will play an important role in bringing them about.

On the question of how to deal with drug addiction there are two opposing schools of thought. The federal Bureau of Narcotics and its supporters regard addiction to narcotic drugs as an activity that is properly subject to police control. With the growth of addiction in the United States since World War II, increasingly severe penalties have been incorporated into both federal and state laws, and the distinction between the peddler of drugs and the user of them has grown smaller and smaller. The advocates of this punitive approach argue that crimes committed by addicts are a direct result of the drug; they also contend that most addicts were criminals before they became addicted.

Critics of this view regard addiction as a disease, or something akin to it, for which punishment is inappropriate. They argue that many addicts become criminals in order to get money to buy drugs, since there is no way in which they can obtain them legally and the cost of illegal procurement is high. This state of affairs, they contend, encourages the spread of addiction among criminals and juvenile delinquents who have easy access to drug peddlers. From this point of view, drug addiction is primarily a problem for the physician rather than for the policeman, and it should not be necessary for anyone to violate the criminal law solely because he is addicted to drugs. This necessity might be avoided by a system of clinics for treating addicts, or by adopting the British practice of permitting physicians to prescribe legal drugs in cases of addiction. Such measures, it is argued, would also remove the stigma of criminality from addiction, and, at the same time, would aid materially in undermining the illicit traffic.

It is understandable that legislators and officials should be reluctant to introduce drastic changes in present laws and practices without long and careful consideration in the light of available factual evidence. The problem deserves careful study. It is of concern to both the legal and the medical profession.

In 1955-56 the American Bar Association and the American Medical Association appointed a Joint Committee on Narcotic Drugs to explore the problem. Its members were: for the American Bar Association, Rufus King (chairman), Judge Edward J. Dimock, and Abe Fortas; for the American Medical Association, Dr. Robert H. Felix, Dr. Isaac Starr, and C. Joseph Stetler. Judge Morris Ploscowe was appointed as director of studies. In 1958 the Joint Committee presented to its two parent bodies an Interim Report surveying various aspects of the narcotic drug question and making recommendations for further research in the future. This Interim Report, with its two lengthy appendices by Judge Ploscowe and Rufus King, forms the main body of the present volume. Also included is the Joint Committee's briefer Final Report, presented in February and June 1959 to the two parent associations, and accepted by the Houses of Delegates of the American Bar Association and the American Medical Association. In accordance with recommendations made by the Joint Committee, the American Bar Association has begun a summary and analysis of existing state and federal laws in the narcotic drug field. Preparations are also under way to carry out other suggested investigations under the auspices of the American Medical Association.

The Joint Committee gave relatively little attention to the role of the medical profession in relation to addiction and to the evolution of national policy on this subject. This was because the Council on Mental Health of the American Medical Association had covered these phases of the subject in a comprehensive report issued in 1956. The summary and recommendations of this report are included in the present volume. The Council's recommendations resemble those of the Joint Committee in that they also reflect dissatisfaction with the operation of existing laws, that they emphasize the medical rather than the punitive approach, that they indicate a positive but cautious attitude toward the possibility of adopting British practices, and that they stress above all the need for more investigation and for more reliable information.

The key document produced by the Joint Committee is the Interim Report, with its appendices. Only a limited number of copies of this document were printed, primarily for use of the Committee itself and for circulation in the Houses of Delegates of the two associations. A few additional copies were printed and sold to persons who requested them. While the work of the Joint Committee, and especially its Final Report, is known to the legal and medical professions, the Interim Report is largely unknown, and the valuable material which it contains has not hitherto been available to the general public.

Another reason for publishing the full work of the Joint Committee is that a comprehensive attack upon it was published in 1959 by the federal Bureau of Narcotics.* The sale of this pamphlet was discontinued after an attack upon the Supreme Court which it contained was given

* *Comments on Narcotic Drugs: Interim Report of the Joint Committee of the American Bar Association and the American Medical Association on Narcotic Drugs by Advisory Committee to the Federal Bureau of Narcotics*, U.S. Treasury Department, Bureau of Narcotics. For sale by the Superintendent of Documents, Government Printing Office, Washington, D.C. 186 pages. 60 cents.

unfavorable newspaper publicity, but by this time the document had already been widely circulated to libraries and law enforcement officials throughout the country. In the meantime, the target of the attack, though it was given some publicity, has become almost unavailable. In view of the discussion and controversy which the Joint Committee's work aroused, it was felt that the reports along with supporting documents should be given circulation equivalent to that enjoyed by the attacks upon them. It is hoped that this book will accomplish that purpose.

The reader may be puzzled by the fact that the Bureau of Narcotics reacted negatively to the work of the Joint Committee. The Bureau is not assailed in the report and is mentioned in only a few places. The language of the report is calm, restrained, objective, and undogmatic. The main emphasis of the recommendations is upon the need for more reliable data, and the experimental project to explore the effects of providing addicts with legal drugs is cautiously stated. If this idea is as dangerous and unsound as its critics contend, the project proposed by the Joint Committee would go a long way toward discrediting it once and for all. This report of the Joint Committee neither states nor implies anything of a derogatory nature concerning the purely law enforcement activities of the Bureau of Narcotics or of the police in general.

The Bureau of Narcotics was established in 1930. The Harrison Anti-Narcotic Act was passed in 1914 and by 1925 the crucial legal questions raised by the Act had been dealt with in the Supreme Court decisions reviewed by Judge Ploscowe. The present pattern of enforcement was thus established before the Bureau was in existence. Even the regulations issued by the Treasury Department for the guidance of enforcement agents had been formulated in substantially their present form before 1930. Certainly the Bureau of Narcotics cannot be held accountable for these early developments, nor does criticism of statutes or of court decisions have any derogatory implications for the police. The police themselves are often among the most vigorous critics of laws which they are called upon to enforce and of court decisions affecting enforcement of such laws.

Rufus King's discussion of foreign practices (Interim Report, Appendix B) is of special interest in view of the fact that before the 1950's very few Americans knew anything about how the drug problem was handled in Britain or in any other European country. During the last ten years interest in British practices and knowledge of what they are have increased greatly,* but profound ignorance is still the rule with respect to the drug control policies of other European nations. For example, with the exception of a few United Nations technical documents, there are no publications which describe the policies, laws, and practices of any of these countries. With respect to Britain the descriptive literature is very sparse, consisting largely of a handful of articles tucked away in professional journals, special reports, and Congressional hearings. One of the reasons for the lack of information is that the drug problem is a very minor one in virtually all European countries, receives little public attention, and is hardly ever mentioned in connection with crime. Discussions of

* A volume entitled *Drug Addiction in Britain and America,* by Edwin M. Schur, will be published in 1962 by Indiana University Press.

it are usually found in medical journals and these ordinarily deal with various technical medical matters rather than with the broad questions of social policy which are debated in the United States.

The debate in the United States during the last ten years or so concerning British practices is a strange one indeed, since it is a debate over what is essentially a simple, easily ascertainable factual matter. While, as Mr. King indicates, there is a difference of opinion between American authorities as to what British practices are, there is no such difference of opinion among the British authorities. The British government has made no secret of its program, the essentials of which are regularly set forth in its annual report to the United Nations and republished by that organization. Nevertheless, for reasons which are indicated in Mr. King's statement, there is still considerable confusion in this country concerning both the nature of the British system and the extent of the drug problem in that country.

For several years most Americans, assuming that American methods of handling addicts were standard practice, have regarded suggestions that addicts be given access to legal drugs as a startling, radical, or dangerous idea. At the same time it has apparently seemed quite normal and acceptable to them that alcohol and barbiturate addicts obtain their supplies legally without police interference, despite the fact that the alcohol and barbiturate habits are probably at least as harmful and more prevalent than is addiction to heroin or morphine. During the years after the war the increased prevalence of addiction stimulated an interest in foreign practices and there has been a growing realization, to which Mr. King's statement should make a substantial contribution, that in reality it is the European practices which are standard rather than the American. The significance of this is enhanced by the fact that even if one accepts the lowest estimates of the number of addicts in this country there would still be more here than in all the countries of Europe combined. Chicago and New York City, with a combined population of about 11 million or one-fifth that of Britain, are ordinarily estimated to have about 30,000 addicts, which is from thirty to fifty times as many as there are said to be in Britain.

The proposals of the Joint Committee are formulated with commendable modesty and caution. Since they call primarily for the collection of more information and for more study of possible alternative programs, they present no inherent obstacles to a joint enterprise involving not only the cooperation of the legal and medical professions but also that of the police and of all other interested groups and individuals. The two basic needs in such an enterprise are full and free investigation and full and free discussion.

ALFRED R. LINDESMITH

December, 1960

Covers of Interim Report and Bureau of Narcotics' reply are reproduced on the following pages.

NARCOTIC DRUGS

INTERIM REPORT

of

THE JOINT COMMITTEE OF THE AMERICAN BAR ASSOCIATION AND THE AMERICAN MEDICAL ASSOCIATION ON NARCOTIC DRUGS

AMERICAN BAR ASSOCIATION

RUFUS KING, ESQ., *Chairman*

JUDGE EDWARD J. DIMOCK

ABE FORTAS, ESQ.

AMERICAN MEDICAL ASSOCIATION

DR. ROBERT H. FELIX

DR. ISAAC STARR

C. JOSEPH STETLER, ESQ.

MORRIS PLOSCOWE

Director Narcotics Control Study

NEW YORK   1958

Cover of Interim Report of the A.B.A.-A.M.A. Joint Committee

Comments on

NARCOTIC DRUGS

INTERIM REPORT OF THE JOINT COMMITTEE

OF THE

AMERICAN BAR ASSOCIATION

AND THE

AMERICAN MEDICAL ASSOCIATION

ON

NARCOTIC DRUGS

BY

Advisory Committee to the Federal Bureau of Narcotics

U. S. TREASURY DEPARTMENT
BUREAU OF NARCOTICS
WASHINGTON, D. C.

Cover of the Bureau of Narcotics' reply to the Interim Report

Narcotic Drugs

INTERIM REPORT

of the Joint Committee of the
American Bar Association and the
American Medical Association
on Narcotic Drugs

INTERIM REPORT

For the last half-century public authorities in the United States have been wrestling with the problem of controlling addiction to narcotic drugs. Since the twenties, legislation and enforcement policies have aimed at total repression, with criminal sanctions of notable severity attaching to every transaction connected with the non-medical use of drugs. Drug-law enforcement has become a major police activity of federal, state and local governments; the threat of long imprisonment, even of death penalties, hangs over not only the smuggler and the peddler, but the addict-victim of the illicit traffic.

Addiction to narcotic substances has been recognized as a health problem for a long time and in many different countries. It has also in our times and in our national com-

3

munity, emerged as a criminal law problem of distressing magnitude and persistency. The fields of medicine and law are thus equally affected, and the Joint Committee which offers this report has undertaken its assignment with enthusiasm at the prospect of uniting its parent organizations in a common effort centered in an area where the concerns of each overlap and largely coincide. If the Joint Committee can contribute something towards mutual enlightenment and ultimate agreement between the medical and legal professions regarding the drug problem, it may clear the way for desirable reforms. But regardless of the final outcome, its work to date has been highly gratifying to those engaged in it simply by virtue of its resounding success as an experiment in close cooperation between the American Medical Association and the American Bar Association.

The Joint Committee warmly acknowledges the participation of another cooperating partner, the Russell Sage Foundation, which contributed substantial material aid to finance the Joint Committee's work. We wish particularly to express our appreciation to Dr. Donald Young and Dr. Leonard S. Cottrell, Jr., of the Foundation, who have followed the Joint Committee's work closely, contributing invaluably from their broad wisdom and experience in the field of social science research.

BACKGROUND

The medical profession in this country was widely concerned about the use and abuse of opiate preparations at least as long ago as the Civil War era. The American

Medical Association supported the enactment of regulatory legislation before the Harrison Act (1914) became law, and its House of Delegates gave active consideration to the development of the federal regulatory pattern in the formulative period 1919-23. A Special Committee on the Narcotic Drug Situation in the United States, appointed pursuant to a resolution of the A. M. A. House of Delegates in June, 1919, studied the situation and submitted an edifying report the following year. A standing Committee on Narcotic Drugs, of the A. M. A. Council on Health and Public Instruction, served actively thereafter.

But except for expressing its position on various matters of administrative detail, the A. M. A. has taken no formal position with regard to the operation of the country's narcotics laws since the adoption, in June, 1924, of a resolution on so-called ambulatory treatment proposed by its Committee on Narcotic Drugs.

In 1954, interest was reawakened by the submission of a proposal from the New York State Medical Society for the legalization of the distribution of narcotics to addicts. The proposal was referred by the A. M. A. House of Delegates to its Council on Pharmacy and Chemistry and Council on Mental Health, and in April, 1955, the latter body appointed a special Committee on Narcotic Addiction, charged with the responsibility of making a thorough study of the matter. Dr. Felix, an A. M. A. member of the Joint Committee, served as chairman of the special committee, which has recently completed its work with a report concluding that the advisability of free distribution cannot be settled on the basis of objective facts at hand, recommending further study and research, and suggesting that the

1924 resolution of the House of Delegates should be revised.

The American Bar Association first concerned itself with narcotic drug laws when its Commission on Organized Crime considered (and disapproved) the mandatory minimum sentences and minimum penalties provided in the first Boggs Act, endorsed by the Kefauver Committee, which became law in 1952. As a result of interest developed in its consideration of these provisions, the A. B. A.'s Section of Criminal Law created a standing Committee on Narcotics and Alcohol. The latter committee, after a survey of federal and state legislation on the subject, proposed a three-part resolution which was passed by the A. B. A. House of Delegates in February, 1955:

"Resolved, That the Section of Criminal Law, through its Chairman or other such appropriate representative as he may appoint, be and it is hereby authorized:
(1) To explore with the American Medical Association the possibilities of a jointly conducted study of the narcotic drug traffic and related problems, by and on behalf of the organizations through their own research facilities or in collaboration with other interested persons or organizations.
(2) To investigate through the American Bar Foundation the availability of funds from sources outside the Association in aid of the study described in the preceding paragraph, and with the approval of the American Bar Foundation to utilize such funds as may be found to be available for that purpose.
(3) To urge the Congress of the United States to undertake a re-examination of the Harrison Act, its amendments and related enforcement and treatment policies and problems."
It is of interest to note with respect to part (3) of the

A. B. A. resolution that the adoption of Senate Resolution 67, authorizing the Daniels Committee study, followed it within a month (84th Congress, 1st Session, March 18, 1955).

Overtures to the American Medical Association through the A. B. A.'s Section of Criminal Law evoked a cordial response, and the project became a truly joint undertaking from the outset. The original appointees to the Joint Committee, Drs. Felix and Starr and Mr. Stetler for the A. M. A., Judge Dimock and Messrs. Fortas and King for the A. B. A., have continued to serve. In the matters of seeking resources for research and organizing its program, the American Bar Foundation, while not participating directly because the subject matter includes non-legal areas, has given the Joint Committee valued guidance and assistance.

WORK OF THE JOINT COMMITTEE

At its first meeting (Washington, March, 1956) the Joint Committee established as its ultimate purpose "to determine whether the two Associations can or should agree upon common principles or a common course of action" with respect to the subject of narcotic drugs. It was decided that the barbiturates, though similar to opiates in some respects, should not be included in the studies at this time. The Joint Committee outlined a number of areas and problems about which factual data seemed lacking, and noted that a considerable amount of research might be required before final conclusions could safely be reached.

During the Summer of 1956, a number of research foundations were approached in quest of advice and support with respect to the Joint Committee's studies. Without exception the responses were approbative, but it was suggested that before seeking any substantial grant of funds, the areas of inquiry ought to be carefully analyzed and reduced to proposals for specific research activity in each case; in the convincing words of one foundation spokesman, "We cannot finance problems—only projects." Thus it was decided to commence on a modest scale with a survey of existing data, an analysis of present conditions and the preparation of one or more specific "project designs." For assistance in making this start, the Joint Committee was most fortunate in being able to reach an agreement with the Russell Sage Foundation of New York.

The Russell Sage Foundation is dedicated to "the improvement of social and living conditions in the United States," differing from many of its counterparts in that it maintains its own research staff and participates directly in many of the undertakings it supports. Its work in recent years has many times entailed cooperation with professional groups, particularly in law, medicine, psychology and psychiatry. Its own general program is currently aimed at increasing the utilization of the social sciences in professional practice.

In October, 1956 a formal application was made to the Russell Sage Foundation for a grant of $15,000 to be used in study of existing data and the preparation of one or more project designs. This application was approved, and the grant made, on November 8, 1956. The Foundation offered the cooperation of its staff, offered to provide office space for the Joint Committee at its headquarters, and undertook to handle all administrative details.

With approval from the A. M. A. Board of Directors and the American Bar Foundation, the Joint Committee accepted these arrangements. At its next meeting (Washington, December, 1956) a respresentative of the Russell Sage Foundation assisted in reviewing the areas to be studied in preparation of the project designs, and the details of procedure were worked out. The Joint Committee next addressed itself to the task of finding a qualified director— a task most fortunately concluded when Judge Morris Ploscowe, formerly director of the A. B. A. Commission on Organized Crime and well known for his studies in the field of crime and criminal law administration, agreed to serve. An important factor in the Joint Committee's selection of Judge Ploscowe was that the Report of the A. M. A. Council on Mental Health on Narcotic Addiction, then just submitted, contained so much excellent material on the medical aspects of addiction that the need for medical research appeared limited and a larger part of the Joint Committee's own work could, it believed, be concentrated on legal, administrative and sociological aspects.

The Joint Committee met again (Philadelphia, March, 1957) with Judge Ploscowe to discuss his undertaking, and at this time, partly in view of the A. M. A. report mentioned above, it was suggested that in some aspects, at least, enough reliable data might be found already available to enable him to reach conclusions in the course of his analysis. Agreement was reached that the work would thus keep three aims in view:

(1) To survey existing sources to find out how much al-

ready existing material was available and could be relied upon;

(2) To determine what experiments and research projects ought to be sponsored by the Joint Committee to remedy deficiencies in present knowledge of the field; and

(3) To draw conclusions, where possible from existing sources, as to any areas which appeared capable of accurate analysis without further study.

REPORTS AND RECOMMENDATIONS

With the foregoing aims in view, a study of the drug addiction problem has gone forward, making use of all available sources and resulting in the report, by Judge Ploscowe, "Some Basic Problems in Drug Addiction and Suggestions for Research," appended hereto as Appendix A. We commend the thoughtful, realistic appraisal of the problems of drug addiction and the critical analysis of present policies toward drug addicts contained in Judge Ploscowe's report. He has clearly spelled out the need for a revision of present attitudes toward and present approaches to drug addicts and drug addiction.

In July-August, 1957, the drug laws and enforcement policies of England and certain European countries were examined, for comparative purposes, by Rufus King, resulting in the report appended hereto as Appendix B.

At its most recent meeting (Washington, November 18, 1957) the Joint Committee considered the aforementioned reports. It approved the substance of the report of Judge

Ploscowe without formally adopting its language or specific appraisals. It agreed to go forward with the preparation of projects in the five specific areas suggested therein, namely:

(1) An Outpatient Experimental Clinic for the Treatment of Drug Addicts (Appendix A, p. 103)

Although it is clear, as the report sets forth, that the so-called clinic approach to drug addiction is the subject of much controversy, the Joint Committee feels that the possibilities of trying some such outpatient facility, on a controlled experimental basis, should be explored, since it can make an invaluable contribution to our knowledge of how to deal with drug addicts in a community, rather than on an institutional basis. It has been suggested that the District of Columbia, being an exclusively federal jurisdiction and immediately accessible to both law-enforcement and public health agencies, might be an advantageous locus for this experiment.

(2) A Study of Relapse and Causative Factors (Appendix A, p. 108)

It is not possible to fully measure the worth of treatment and rehabilitation measures without more data than has yet been accumulated on the rate of relapse, and on the causative factors underlying both addiction and successful rehabilitation. The Joint Committee feels that large scale research in this area (complementing several limited studies which are already under way) would be highly desirable. Such research is absolutely indispensable to any thorough-going evaluation of present policies in dealing with narcotic addiction, as well as to the formulation of new approaches in dealing with this difficult problem.

(3) Educational and Preventative Research (Appendix A, p. 109)

The dissemination of accurate information about narcotic addiction has been neglected and even discouraged by some enforcement authorities. The Joint Committee feels that this matter should be studied critically, to determine whether a campaign of enlightenment might not produce good results. The Joint Committee also feels that other preventative techniques can be devised which can aid materially in lowering the incidence of drug addiction.

(4) Legal Research (Appendix A, p. 113)

There is uncertainty at present both in the ambiguous provisions of some of our narcotic drug statutes and in the court decisions through which they have been applied. There is also doubt as to whether the premises on which our present narcotic laws rest are sound and validly conceived. A critical study in this area would make possible a thorough evaluation of present legal approaches to narcotic addiction. It should result in the formulation of better methods for dealing with the addict and more realistic and sounder means for controlling the illicit drug traffic.

(5) Research in the Administration of Present Laws (Appendix A, p. 111)

There is considerable uncertainty and confusion in the enforcement of existing drug laws. This may be inherent in the nature of the laws, procedures or administrative and judicial machinery which seeks to enforce them. A careful study of how existing laws are operating should provide invaluable guides for a rational drug control program in this country.

THE PROGRAM AHEAD

The five areas described above are those in which the Joint Committee intends to develop specific project designs for its research. This step, to be taken next, is still within the compass of the Russell Sage Foundation grant, and will occupy the Joint Committee's director and cooperating staff until completed. When the designs are complete, additional funds will be sought to carry them out. In some cases, they may appropriately be turned over to other organizations and agencies; for example, it is contemplated that the resources of the American Bar Foundation could be utilized for the legal-research projects.

It is anticipated that another work of value will be completed while the research projects are being developed: a selected bibliography of current material on narcotic drugs has been collected for the Joint Committee and this, plus a carefully edited set of selected readings, will be submitted for publication, if approved, by the Russell Sage Foundation.

The Joint Committee still holds its basic aim, namely, to determine whether the two Associations can agree upon common principles, or a common course of action, with respect to the narcotic drug problem. Its final report will contain its conclusions on this subject as well as its statement of principles and recommended action. But until more is learned about the narcotic problem—until at least some of the proposed research is completed—the Joint Committee believes it should proceed slowly. No final conclusions are therefore offered at this time and no time-table of future progress is attempted. Unless otherwise directed, the Joint Committee will carry on at its present pace until it is satisfied that the assignment given to it has been fully carried out.

RUFUS KING, Chairman
JUDGE EDWARD J. DIMOCK
ABE FORTAS
DR. ROBERT H. FELIX
DR. ISAAC STARR
C. JOSEPH STETLER

APPENDIX A

Some Basic Problems in Drug Addiction and Suggestions for Research*

by MORRIS PLOSCOWE

I. INTRODUCTION—SEVERITY OF PUNISHMENT AS DETERRENCE TO DRUG ADDICTION

In 1914 Congress, with the passage of the Harrison Act, embarked upon a policy of prohibiting legal access to narcotic drugs on the part of those addicted to such drugs. This prohibitory policy has been strengthened by subsequent legislation. It has been implemented with considerable vigor by the Narcotics Bureau of the Treasury Department and by other state and local enforcement agencies throughout the country, acting under the authority of state

* The author wishes to express his deep appreciation to Miss Margo Moraitis for her intelligent and painstaking assistance in the preparation of this report. The author also wishes to express his gratitude to the staff of the Russell Sage Foundation for their unfailing cooperation.

15

and local statutes. Despite this effort, a Senate Committee[1]
recently came to the conclusion that, "The United States
has more narcotic addicts, both in total numbers and popu-
lation-wise, than any other country of the Western World."

Such a finding, that we have more drug addicts than any
other Western country, despite forty years of enforcement
of prohibitory laws, raises doubts concerning the wisdom
of the prohibitory approach to problems of drug addiction.
It would seem to require a re-examination of our narcotics
policy. Nevertheless, the two Congressional Committees[2]
which recently conducted nationwide inquiries into problems of drug addiction and the drug traffic appeared to be
oblivious to doubts concerning the wisdom of the current
policy toward narcotic drugs.* Both Committees took the
basic position that even stronger prohibitions were required if our narcotic addiction problems were to be satisfactorily controlled.

Three basic concepts run through the recommendations
of both Congressional Committees: (1) more stringent narcotic law enforcement; (2) severer penalties for offenders
against the narcotic laws; (3) the permanent isolation of
incurable drug addicts. The thinking of the Committees is
contained in the following extracts from their reports:

"Effective control of the vicious narcotic traffic requires not
only vigorous enforcement, but also certainty of punishment.
Conclusive evidence was presented during your sub-committee's

---

* The first inquiry was conducted by a House Committee under the
Chairmanship of Hale Boggs; the second by a Senate Committee under
the Chairmanship of Price Daniel. Both Committees made determined
efforts to get at the facts surrounding drug addiction and the drug traffic
in this country. The printed records of the testimony taken run into
several thousand pages.

investigation that the imposition of heavier penalties was the strongest deterrent to narcotic addiction and narcotic traffic." . . .

"Unless immediate action is taken to prohibit probation or suspension of sentence, it is the sub-committee's considered opinion that the first offender peddler problem will become eventually worse and eventually lead to the large scale recruiting of our youth by the upper echelon of traffickers." . . .

"Some testimony received by the sub-committee that . . . a distinction should be made between the non-addict trafficker and the addict trafficker, with the latter group being dealt with less severely. It is the view of your sub-committee that the addict trafficker is just as vicious a person as the non-addict trafficker." . . .

"It is urged . . . that the minimum and maximum penalties applicable to conviction for violations of the narcotic laws be increased on both the federal and state levels."[3]

"Criminal laws and procedures are insufficient to insure the apprehension and punishment of narcotics offenders." . . .

"Penalties for narcotic violations are neither commensurate with the seriousness of the crime nor sufficient to remove the profits." . . .

"The minimum and maximum penalties be increased for all violations of the narcotics law, with greatly increased penalties for sales to juveniles." . . .[4]

"The Committee has found that whenever and wherever penalties are severe and strictly enforced drug addiction and narcotic trafficking have decreased proportionately." . . .[5]

"That habitual narcotic addicts be committed to 'an indeterminable quarantine type of confinement on a suitable narcotics farm'." . . .[6]

The Report to the President of the Inter-Departmental Committee On Narcotics[7] also stresses the vital importance of severe punishment as a basic means of controlling drug addiction and the drug problem.

"The Committee has arrived at the conclusion that there is need for a continuation of the policy of punishment of a severe character as a deterrent to narcotic law violations. It therefore recommends an increase of maximum sentences for first as well as subsequent offenses. With respect to the mandatory minimum features of such penalties and prohibitions of suspended sentences or probation, the Committee fully recognizes the objections in principle. It feels however that in order to define the gravity of this class of crime and the assured penalty to follow, these features of the law must be regarded as essential elements of the desired deterrents, although some difference of opinion still exists regarding their application to first offenses of certain types."[8]

These predilections for stringent law enforcement and severer penalties as answers to the problems of drug addiction reflect the philosophy and the teachings of the Bureau of Narcotics. For years the Bureau has supported the doctrine that if penalties for narcotic drug violations were severe enough and if they could be enforced strictly enough, drug addiction and the drug traffic would largely disappear from the American scene. This approach to problems of narcotics has resulted in spectacular modifications of our narcotic drug laws on both the state and federal level.

The 84th Congress passed legislation which provided that whoever "receives, conceals, buys or sells" heroin, etc., shall be punished by 5 to 10 years' imprisonment for a first offense. The giving, selling or furnishing of heroin to a person under 18 years of age was made punishable by sentences of 10 years to life or the death sentence if directed by the jury. Legal provisions permitting suspended sentence and probation for violations of the drug laws were struck from the federal statutes.

The states have followed the lead of the Federal Government in strengthening penalties for violations of the drug laws. In California, unlawful possession of narcotics was formerly punishable by a maximum of 6 years in the State prison. A 1953 amendment increased the maximum to 10 years and to 20 years for a second offense. In Illinois, illicit possession of a narcotic drug used to be punished by a maximum of one year in the County jail. It is now punishable by 2 to 10 years in the penitentiary for a first offense, and 5 years to life for subsequent offenses. In Michigan, unlawful possession of narcotic drugs was punishable by a maximum of 4 years imprisonment. At present, such possession is punishable by a maximum of 10 years for a first offense, 20 years for a second offense, and 29 to 40 years for a third offense. In Ohio, unlawful possession of drugs was punishable by a maximum of 5 years imprisonment. Today, the penalties for unlawful possession as a first offense are 2 to 15 years, for a second offense, 5 to 20 years, and for a third offense, 10 to 30 years.

Stringent law enforcement has its place in any system of controlling narcotic drugs. However, it is by no means the complete answer to American problems of drug addiction. In the first place it is doubtful whether drug addicts can be deterred from using drugs by threats of jail or prison sentences. The belief that fear of punishment is a vital factor in deterring an addict from using drugs rests upon a superficial view of the drug addiction process and the nature of drug addiction. This will be apparent from the discussion of the nature and mechanics of drug addiction (see *infra*). It is also doubtful whether it will be possible to incarcerate indefinitely relapsing, uncured drug addicts as recommended by the Senate Committee. The Committee urged this step because of the fear that incurable drug addicts carry the contagion of drug addiction to others. In order to prevent such contagion, incurable drug addicts must be permanently incarcerated and permanently isolated from the community. There are thousands of men and women in this country who are confirmed drug addicts and who are incurable by present methods and techniques. If the Senate Committee recommendation is to be acted upon, places of detention will have to be set up for these thousands of men and women, by Congress and state legislatures. There is little likelihood that federal and state legislation will provide new places of detention for large numbers of confirmed drug addicts. Men and women may jam our prisons and penitentiaries for alleged violations of the drug laws. But it is not likely that in the foreseeable future there will be any wholesale round-up of chronic and incurable drug addicts for more or less permanent isolation.

Since all confirmed addicts cannot be incarcerated, permanently, there will always be addicts at liberty to serve as customers for an illicit drug traffic. Even where drug addicts are sentenced to penal or correctional institutions, they eventually come out. They may be off the drug when in the institution but they usually relapse to the use of drugs shortly after they are released from institutional confinement. Severe penalties and strict enforcement may deter or discourage some drug peddlers. But there will always be others attracted by the lure of the large profits to be made in the drug traffic. The very severity of law enforcement tends to increase the price of drugs on the illicit market and the profits to be made therefrom. The lure of profits and the risks of the traffic simply challenge the ingenuity of the underworld peddlers to find new channels of distribution and new customers, so that profits can be maintained despite the risks involved. So long as a non-addict peddler is willing to take the risk of serving as a wholesaler of drugs, he can always find addict pushers or peddlers to handle the retail aspects of the business in return for a supply of the drugs for themselves.* Thus, it is the belief of the author of this report that no matter how severe law enforcement may be, the drug traffic cannot be eliminated under present prohibitory repressive statutes.

Moreover, even if it were [theoretically] possible to eliminate the drug traffic through strict and uniform enforcement of narcotic laws, this objective is practically unreal-

---

* It should be noted that on occasion, law enforcement agencies themselves may act as suppliers of drugs to addicts. The greater the pressure upon law enforcement agencies, the greater the necessity of producing arrests in drug cases. Arrests in drug cases cannot be made without information. Stool pigeons or informers are vital suppliers of information. Nobody is better equipped to provide information concerning violations of the narcotic drug laws than the narcotic addict himself. One pays off the stool pigeon in money, in winking at his illegal activity, and in the case of the addict, sometimes in seeing that he obtains his drugs. Thus it has been alleged that the law enforcement agencies that are engaged in enforcing the narcotic laws may themselves see that drugs are supplied to addicts.

izable. In the first place, inefficiency in law enforcement is endemic in this country. The causes are many and varied. Among such causes are inadequate recruiting and training of police officials, lack of specialized expert direction of police departments, political selection of police chiefs and district attorneys, part time and amateur administration in district attorney's offices and courts, political selection of judges, lack of coordination between law enforcement agencies, lack of State supervision of local law enforcement, conflicts between uncoordinated law enforcement agencies, inadequacies in the law of arrest, search and seizure, and other branches of procedural law, etc.

Any particular community can overcome the factors contributing to inefficient law enforcement and stage a concerted drive against drug addicts and drug peddlers. Such a drive can result in imprisoning many individuals. But it will also bring about an exodus of drug addicts and drug peddlers to communities where the "heat" is not on, and where law enforcement is a little more lax and lenient. So long as our law enforcement agencies consist of thousands of independent units, there will always be communities where the enforcement of the drug laws will be viewed with relative indifference and where drug addicts and drug peddlers can wait out a flurry of law enforcement in their own communities.

Strict law enforcement and severe penalties are therefore not the easy answers to problems of drug addiction. We must look elsewhere for a rational drug control program for this country. Any such program must be based on a thorough understanding of the phenomenon that we are seeking to control. Failure to understand the nature of the phenomenon of drug addiction and the practical problems involved in controlling it are responsible for the fact that drug addiction has such serious consequences in this country.

II. THE DEFINITION OF DRUG ADDICTION

An authoritative definition of drug addiction is that propounded by the World Health Organization:

"Drug addiction is a state of periodic and chronic intoxication detrimental to the individual and to society, produced by the repeated consumption of a drug (natural or synthetic). Its characteristics include:
(1) An overpowering desire or need (compulsion) to continue taking the drug and to obtain it by any means;
(2) A tendency to increase the dose;
(3) A psychic (psychological) and sometimes a physical dependence on the effects of the drug."

This definition of drug addiction includes many drugs which are not within the scope of our study, such as hypnotic and sedative drugs (barbiturates, etc.) alcohol, amphetamine, mescaline (peyote).[9]

We are interested primarily in the abuse of the opiate drugs and the synthetic-like opiates, such as heroin, morphine, opium, laudanum dilaudid, codeine, demerol, etc. We are not engaged in anthropological investigation. Accordingly, we shall not study the abuse of mescaline or peyote, which is of little practical importance in this country and is used primarily by Indians in the Southwest for religious rites. We shall, however, pay some attention to

cocaine and marihuana, which are included within the
above definition, even though the effects of cocaine or
marihuana differ from the opiate drugs. Cocaine is sometimes used alone. It is, however, frequently used as a con-
comitant of opiate addiction to obtain a special kind of
thrill (speedball). The use of marihuana frequently pre-
cedes experimentation with the more powerful drugs, such
as heroin. Neither cocaine nor marihuana, however, produces the characteristic withdrawal syndrome resulting
from physical dependence on the opiates.

We shall not deal with the abuse of alcohol, even though
there are many more alcoholics in the United States than
opiate addicts. Nor shall we deal with the barbiturates or
the amphetamine problem, even though two Congressional
Committees were concerned with their abuse. The legal,
though regulated, distribution of alcohol, the barbiturates
and amphetamine drugs presents a different set of problems from the complete prohibition of the non medical use
and sale of the opiate drugs.* There are those who believe
that the legal attitude of strict prohibition of the non medical use of opiate drugs is largely responsible for the character of the drug addiction problems in this country.

The prime drug of addiction in this country is heroin.
There is a great deal of use and experimentation with
heroin, which does not quite fall within the above defini-

* We should note, however, that addiction to and intoxication with
alcohol or the barbiturates may produce withdrawal symptoms or an
abstinence syndrome which is the characteristic of opiate addiction.
Addiction to barbiturates, moreover, may be even more dangerous and
harmful than addiction to morphine or to an opium derivative. (See for
example Nyswander, *The Drug Addict As A Patient*, Grune & Stratton,
p. 126.)

tion of the World Health Organization. There are many persons, particularly in the slum areas of our large cities, who have the drug habit—who use drugs more or less regularly, but who have not become addicted. While they may have become psychologically dependent upon heroin, they are not physically dependent upon it and deprivation of heroin may not, in these individuals, produce the characteristic withdrawal symptoms which appear whenever an addict to an opiate drug fails to obtain his usual "fix".

This is illustrated by the following comments of the N. Y. U. study, "Heroin Use and Street Gangs":

"Heroin addiction is typified by regular use, increased tolerance and physical dependence. An addict uses at least one dose of heroin (or another drug) every day and his intake increases with time. Yet we find that not all of the 94 heroin users studied are seriously dependent upon the drug, even though most of them have been taking heroin for 2-3 years. For one thing, only 43% take one or more doses of heroin daily; only these can be presumed addicted. The rest take the drug two or three times a week or even less often and many of them remain on this non-addictive level, even though some of them inject directly into a vein. Furthermore, only about half of them (54%) use the drug intravenously. Such casual or weekend use represents a type that is not usually encountered in the medical literature because such users do not show the typical characteristics of addiction, tolerance and physical dependence. For this group, heroin use may be largely a social activity, the drug being taken as part of the leisure time patterns the boys have adopted."

The terrific adulteration of the drugs sold may explain this phenomenon of use and experimentation with heroin without addiction. A Chicago police officer testified before the Senate Committee:

"You see now there is something else. When we test the stuff in our crime laboratory, the quality is over 2%, what they are getting is all milk sugar. I remember years ago, back in 1928 and 1929, an addict would get a cap and it would last him 2 days because it was 50% or 60% pure . . .

"Here is something else that is very important. We have these addicts every day in our bureau and very seldom do we get an addict that is sick. They are all needle addicts. It is just a rare case of where we have an addict that is really sick and going through a withdrawal period."[10]

A similar phenomenon was noted for Detroit:

"I have tested 1,422 addicts . . . I would assume that there are at least half as many addicts unknown to us . . . and when we refer to addicts . . . we are covering marihuana smokers, occasional and the regular type, people who are not really addicted. They are occasional users, what we call 'joy poppers', lightly addicted people. And the drugs in Michigan . . . are terrifically adulterated. The average capsule of heroin on the street is almost 1½ to 3% . . . In other words, a lot of addicts are taking voluntary cures in this city." . . .[11]

Were it not for the aforementioned adulteration, our drug addict problem would be much more serious than it is at present. The greed of peddlers of narcotics has saved many from a full blown addiction. Nevertheless, there can be little doubt that much addiction results from the occasional or weekend use of drugs like heroin, even where the drugs are greatly adulterated.

III. THE EXTENT OF DRUG ADDICTION

It is impossible to give any exact estimates of the number of drug addicts in this country. Nor can one with full confidence determine the basic question as to whether drug addiction is increasing or decreasing. The strong social disapproval of the use of opiate drugs and the police pressures against drug users and traffickers necessarily cause drug addicts and drug takers to conceal themselves from strange or unfriendly eyes. They do not come into the open to be counted. Any statistics with respect to the extent of drug addiction must, therefore, usually be based on apprehended addicts or apprehended users of drugs. If we knew what proportion of drug addicts or users are arrested every year, we would have a reasonable basis for estimating the extent of drug addiction in this country. Unfortunately, we do not know the proportion that arrested drug addicts or drug users bear to the total addict and user population. Moreover, increases or decreases in the number of arrests are just as likely to reflect increases or decreases in police activity rather than an increase or decrease in drug use or drug addiction. A further complication is the fact that a person arrested as a drug user may not necessarily be an addict, even though he may be so classified by the police. Thus, any statements with respect to the extent of drug addiction and its changes from year to year must be viewed with a considerable degree of reserve and caution.

In 1924, Dr. Lawrence Kolb and A. G. DuMez[12] conducted a survey of the extent of narcotic addiction for the Public Health Service. They came to the conclusion, on the basis of an analysis of surveys of narcotics use, reports on narcotics clinics, statistics on narcotics imported into this country, interviews with physicians and other data that the maximum number of addicts in the U. S. was 150,000. However, Kolb and DuMez believed that the figure of 110,000 addicts for the country in 1924 was more "nearly correct." They also believed that the number of addicts had decreased steadily since 1900. Before this decrease set in there may have been 264,000 addicts in this country. The careful analysis of Kolb and DuMez was criticized by Terry and Pellens, who believed that this estimate of 110,000 addicts for the country was too low:

"We cannot agree that the ultimate estimate of 110,000 is warranted. While we on the one hand deplore sensational exaggerations, on the other hand we recognize the danger of basing maximal estimates on selected data."[13]

Until the second World War, the reports of the Bureau of Narcotics were full of statements concerning the reduction in drug addiction. For example, the 1935 report states:

"This recent survey shows that the total number of non medical addicts in the U. S. has decreased to the extent that there is now less than one addict known to the authorities in every thousand of the population."[14]

A similar comment is found in the 1937 report:

"From the present study it is evident that addiction has decreased to the extent that there are now less than two addicts known to the authorities in every 10,000 of the population."[15]

Shortly after the second World War, the use of narcotic drugs appeared to have spread with epidemic force in the slum areas of our large cities, particularly among minority groups of the population. Negroes and Puerto Ricans were especially involved in this increasing use of narcotic drugs, particularly heroin. We do not have any specific statistics on the Puerto Ricans, but the fact that large numbers of Negroes were arrested in recent years for violations of the narcotics laws is apparent from the following figures. In Chicago in 1954, there was a total of 7,639 narcotics arrests; 6,601 of these were Negro arrests, 752 were White arrests and 286 were classified as "other races." In Detroit in the year 1955, of a total of 1,812 arrests, for violations of the narcotics laws, 1,593 were classified as Negroes; 184 were classified as White; 12 were classified as "Yellow"; and 23 were classified as Mexican. The Bureau of Narcotics made a survey of addicts in the United States in the year 1953-1954. Its report noted a total of 6,957 addicts in the Illinois, Indiana and Wisconsin areas; of this number 6,057 were Negro; 916 were listed as Caucasian and 2 were listed as Oriental. In the New York, New Jersey area, of a total of 7,937 addicts, 4,740 were listed as Negro; 3,037 were listed as White, and 160 were listed as Orientals. It should be noted that the ratio of male to female among the persons arrested for violation of the drug laws is approximately 5 to 1.*

The most disturbing feature of the increasing resort to the use of narcotic drugs in the post-war period was the apparently increasing use of heroin by adolescents and "teenagers." As the Boggs Committee put it:

* For example, in Chicago in the year of 1954, of the 7,639 arrests for violation of the narcotic laws 6,182 were male and 1,457 were female. In New York in 1956, of a total of 6,093 arrests, 5,032 were male and 1,061 were female. In Detroit in the year 1955, there were 1,812 arrests of which 1,454 were male and 318 were female.

"In 1948 an upsurge in addiction and an outbreak of teen-age use of narcotic drugs occurred. By 1950, narcotic addiction approached grave proportions in certain metropolitan areas of the country."[16]

A similar conclusion was reached by the New York Attorney General's Survey, 1952:

"The investigation revealed with disturbing clarity that
(a) Narcotic use and addiction . . . has increased in tremendous fashion since World War II and particularly in the last two years.
(b) The disease has spread with alarming rapidity through the ranks of our adolescent society."[17]

A Chicago study of drug addiction made in 1952 determined that there were 5,310 individual drug addicts in the City of Chicago, "slightly more than 1/10th of 1% of Chicago's 1950 population." *Upwards of 90% of these persons acquired records as drug addicts during the five years 1947-1952.* Males made up 83% of this drug user and addict population. Moreover, more than 4/5ths (84.1%) were non-white.

Public concern with the apparent increase in the use of drugs after World War II led to a spectacular rise in arrests for violations of the narcotic drug laws. Arrests for violations of narcotic laws appear in the table on pages 32-33.

It is apparent from the table below that arrests for narcotics violations of all types in New York were 712 in 1946 as against 5,965 in 1956; in Chicago the comparable figures were 424 and 9,011; in Los Angeles, 1,166 and 5,091; in Detroit, 339 and 2,646.

There appears to be little doubt that drugs like heroin

were readily available in many of the slum areas of our larger cities in the post-war years, despite considerable pressure from law enforcement. This availability of heroin, together with a social and cultural climate in the areas which favored drug use, undoubtedly encouraged many teen-agers and many young adults to try heroin. This experimentation with drugs like heroin must have inevitably increased the drug addict population in this country. Just how much of an increase has resulted from the increased availability and the increased experimentation with heroin, it is difficult to say.

Despite the difficulties in determining the exact number of addicts in the country, the need for data on the extent of the problem has brought about a considerable acceptance of the Bureau of Narcotics' statement that there are almost 60,000 addicts in the country.[18] This estimate was accepted as reasonably accurate in the report to the President of the Inter-Departmental Committee on Narcotics.[19]

"Many and varied estimates have been made as to the number of persons in the U. S. addicted to narcotic drugs. The Committee regards the current estimate of the Bureau of Narcotics as the most accurate available. This estimate of 60,000 is based on the records of its own agents and cooperating state and municipal authorities."

"While there are far less drug addicts in the Nation today than there were before the Harrison Narcotics Act was passed and before the Federal Bureau of Narcotics was created, the figure of 60,000 addicts today is far more than the number reported by other western nations."

There are indications that this estimate of 60,000 narcotics addicts for this country is too low. For example, a

| | | | NUMBER OF ARRESTS FOR | |
	1946	1947	1948	1949
New York	712	1,014	1,305	1,410
Chicago	424	331	422	647
Los Angeles	1,166	1,573	1,590	1,373
Detroit	339	438	363	786
Baltimore		52	130	65
Washington, D. C.	48	58	39	100
Boston	121	120	94	147
San Francisco	316	323	329	561
Milwaukee	4	0	0	48
Cincinnati	10	8	9	12

recent California report to the Attorney General on Narcotic Addiction stated:

"What is the extent of addiction in California? No one knows with any degree of accuracy. It is known that we have in our State medical files some 32,000 persons who are legally using narcotics medicinally, although a certain percentage of them may be using it illegally because they are going to several different doctors concurrently. The state criminal files reflect that there are approximately 10,000 additional illegal traffickers or users of narcotics in California. It is believed that 10,000 represents approximately one-half of the total illegal addicts in this State. Our estimated total, therefore, would be 32,000 medical or legal users and probably 20,000 illegal, a total of 52,000 persons."[20]

If it is true that there are at least 20,000 illegal users of opiate drugs in California alone, then it is questionable that there are only 40,000 more addicts in the rest of the United States. It appears to be obvious that the exact number of drug addicts in this country is unknown. However, it is apparent that whatever the extent of drug addic-

NARCOTIC LAW VIOLATION

1950	1951	1952	1953	1954	1955	1956
2,482	3,634	2,959	3,588	4,296	5,216	5,965
967	6,742	7,436	8,267	7,639	7,454	9,011
2,152	2,651	2,909	3,839	4,309	4,690	5,091
1,142	1,741	1,534	1,616	1,706	2,153	2,646
118	301	169	131	205	290	279
70	12	15	270	215	231	175
110	131	186	296	305	394	425
711	796	820	695	500	503	442
78	152	174	151	157	196	226
12	75	90	44	87	97	87

tion in this country may be, as Terry and Pellens pointed out almost 30 years ago:

"The surveys and estimates indicate sufficiently the existence of a major medical-social problem. . . . As a matter of fact it is not necessary to know the exact number of users or even the minimal extent to realize *that there are a large number in the country and that the problem is serious.*"[21]

IV. THE NATURE AND CHARACTERISTICS OF DRUG ADDICTION

The law has largely acted on the premise, which is supported by some of the earlier writers, that drug addiction was largely a vice, which an effort of the will could conquer. Severe penalties were necessary to compel the will to make the effort to conquer the vice. Medical writers, on the other hand, have taken the view that drug addiction was a disease and that the drug addict was a sick person. For example, Ernest S. Bishop wrote many years ago:

"The fundamental truth which applies to all cases of narcotic drug addiction is this—whatever may have been the circumstances of the primary administration of narcotic drugs, or whatever the physical, ethical or personal status of the person addicted . . . Continued administration of the drug creates within the body of the person to whom the drug is administered a physical disease process. A demonstration of material cause and effect in obvious symptomatology, in physical suffering, and in nerve strain and exhaustion, unless there is applied to that person in sufficient amounts the drug of his addiction. Every addict is sick of a disease condition . . . insufficiently recognized and insufficiently studied."[22]

Or as Dr. William G. Somerville put it:

"Drug addiction is a disease, a pathological condition just as much as the psychoneuroses of any of the various toxic states."[23]

If the physiological and psychological need for the drug inherent in drug addiction is a disease, then it will be apparent from our discussion of relapse that it is a disease which is largely incurable by present methods and techniques. The course of the disease can only be controlled by the continued administration of the drug of addiction or some similar drug.

There are, however, many who do not regard drug addiction as a disease entity. Maurer and Vogel for example have pointed out that:

"All the research done on drug addiction within the past two generations indicates that addiction is not a disease, rather a symptom of personality difficulties, which if they did not lead to drug addiction would lead to difficulties of other types."[24]

Maurer and Vogel would say that drug addicts are sick, unbalanced, disturbed, abnormal individuals. Unfortunately as we shall see in our discussion of the personality types of drug addicts (*infra*), it is easier to attach a psychopathological label to the drug addict than to explain how or why he became addicted or why he continues his addiction. Many with similar psychological difficulties do not become addicted to drugs. Some become alcoholics rather than drug addicts. The mere designation of a drug addict as a sick, unbalanced, disturbed or abnormal individual conceals more than it reveals. This is clearly indicated by the comments of Dr. H. Isbell:

"Addiction is a complex process in which pharmacological, psychological, socio-economic and legal factors play interdependent roles. It is viewed in two ways: (1) as a distinct disease; (2) as a symptom of an underlying personality disorder. Both views can be supported by evidence established so far. Studies have shown that the majority of addicts have personality disorders which antedate drug use. Also, addicts use many drugs and change from one to another especially when their favorite drug is difficult to obtain. Drugs used by addicts also have diverse actions; they not only use drugs that cause 'depression' but also stimulants. The only common denominator among drugs abused by addicts seems to be that they all are compounds which exert powerful effects on the central nervous system. These facts suggest that there is nothing specific about the drugs that addicts take and, therefore, addiction is nothing more than a symptom of the personality disorder. This view cannot be accepted without reservation. The theories of personality that are used to explain addiction are the same theories that are used to explain neurosis, psychoses, character disorders, etc. Since it is known that many persons with personality characteristics similar to those of addicts never abuse drugs, it is apparent that factors other than personality must be operating. Furthermore, under conditions of equal drug exposure, one individual may choose opiates, another alcohol. This implies some sort of specificity in the choice of the drug of addiction."[25]

Whether addiction to drugs be viewed as a disease or as a symptom of personality disorder it usually involves the three characteristically related phenomena, noted in the definition of the World Health Organization, namely, (1) tolerance, (2) physical dependence and (3) emotional dependence. These phenomena have been described by Isbell and White as follows:

"By tolerance is meant a decreasing effect on repetition of the same dose of a drug. This particular characteristic is very marked in addiction to the opiates and synthetic analgesics. Patients with well developed tolerance have injected as much as 5 gm. (78 gr.) of morphine sulfate intravenously in less than twenty-four hours without developing significant toxic symptoms. Tolerance to the various effects of morphine and related drugs develops, however, at different rates and in different degrees. For example, tolerance to the toxic, sedative, emetic, analgesic and respiratory-depressant effects of morphine develops very rapidly and becomes marked, whereas tolerance to the miotic effects and to the spasmogenic effects on gastro-intestinal smooth muscle, if developed at all, is never complete.

"Physical dependence refers to the development of an altered physiologic state which requires continued administration of a drug to prevent the appearance of a characteristic illness, termed an 'abstinence syndrome.' Physical dependence is an extremely important characteristic of addiction to morphine and similar drugs, since it leads to continuity of intoxication with resultant subservience of all phases of the addict's life to the one aim of obtaining and maintaining a constant supply of the drug.

"Emotional dependence is defined as a substitution of the use of the drug for other types of adaptive behavior. In other words, use of the drug becomes the answer to all of life's problems. Instead of taking constructive action about his difficulties, regardless of their type, the addict seeks refuge in his drug."[26]

It is simpler to describe the phenomenon of tolerance to and physical dependence upon opiate drugs, as Isbell and White have done, than to explain the exact mechanics of their action upon the human organism. A great deal of research has been done on both phenomena in the attempt to find such explanations. Much of value has been uncovered by this research. Nevertheless, the fundamental effects of narcotic drugs upon the human system are still obscure. As Maurer and Vogel have noted:

"The action of the opiate drugs and their synthetic equivalents upon human beings is still imperfectly understood. This fact is striking when we consider that opium has been used generally for thousands of years, and that no single medicine is more useful or more generally used by the physician than the modern opium derivatives and opium-like synthetics . . . Certain fundamental questions are still unanswered; many peripheral or incidental problems remain to be solved. With some of the basic reactions of opiates upon the human physiology and neurology still obscure, it is not surprising that the nature of addiction to drugs of the opiate series . . . should still be a controversial matter. *The nature of narcotic addiction is still not yet fully understood.*"*[27]

The present status of research on tolerance and dependence is clearly summarized by Isbell, in his authoritative article, "Trends Research On Opiate Addiction."

"Most physiological research in addiction has been concerned with tolerance and physical dependence. Two major hypotheses have been developed. The first is that of Tatum, Seevers and Collins and is based on the dual character of the effects of morphine on the central nervous system. Morphine has both

---

* An examination of Nathan A. Eddy's classic chapter on tolerance and addiction, which summarizes the studies up to 1940, indicates the soundness of the above observation. Dr. Eddy wrote as follows:

"The last word has not been said by any means on the mechanism of tolerance and addiction to morphine. Evidence is accumulating that morphine is handled differently in the tolerant animal. In addition, the phasic character of morphine action (excitation on the one hand, and apparent depression on the other hand), seems to be intimately concerned in the tolerance development and addiction, whether it is a question of the time relations of the two effects or of an alteration of the biologic substrate. The disturbed autonomic and hormone balance in addiction and withdrawal needs further careful thorough study."[28]

Commenting on tolerance, Dr. Eddy stated:

"The evidence as a whole points to a change in the cells of the nervous system as the important factor, but the exact nature of the change and its fundamental mechanism are still unknown."

In the same volume as Dr. Eddy's study, Margaret Sumwalt analyzed the studies which attempted to answer the question of what the organism does to morphine. She pointed out that man disposed of between $\frac{1}{3}$ to $\frac{1}{10}$ of his intake of morphine in his urine and feces. Sweat and saliva carry trivial amounts. Milk perhaps more.

"The remaining 65 to 85% is got rid of rather promptly by unknown chemical processes . . . *The chemistry of morphine metabolism is unknown.*"[29]

excitant and depressant effects within the central nervous system. In animals, the excitant effects appear to outlast the depressant effects. Therefore, as morphine is repeatedly administered, the excitant effects constantly increase. This excess excitation requires more and more of the drug in order to obtain the excitant effects, which are still present, and unopposed by depressant effects; hence, abstinence symptoms occur. Recently this hypothesis has been expanded. It is conceived that morphine exerts its depressant effects by attachment to receptors within the cells. The drug at receptor sites on the cell surface is in equilibrium with drugs in body fluids, is easily detached and swiftly metabolized. Morphine hypothetically diffuses into and out of cells quite slowly, so that degradation of drug attached at this site is slow. Since drugs on the cell surface are more rapidly dissipated than are drugs within the cells, the excitant effects outlast the depressant. Unfortunately this concept is completely untestable with present technics, and there are also objections to the 'depressant-excitant' formulation. In the lower animals, codeine is a more excitant drug than is morphine. One would therefore, assume that symptoms of abstinence from codeine would be more severe than symptoms of abstinence from morphine; actually, the reverse is the case. Also, in the chronic spinal dog, morphine markedly enhances—'stimulates'—the ipsilateral extensor thrust reflex.

"If this is regarded as an excitant action of morphine, the reflex should be even more hyperactive following withdrawal of the drug. Actually, the extensor thrust reflex disappears during abstinence.

"The other theory of tolerance and physical dependence was first formulated by Joel and Ettinger and has been further developed by Himmelsbach. In this formulation, it is hypothesized that the administration of morphine calls into play homeostatic responses which oppose the effects—chiefly the depressant effects—of the morphine. These homeostatic responses are gradually strengthened by repeated administration of the drug and, therefore, more drug is required to induce the initial degree of effect. When morphine is removed, the enhanced homeostatic responses still remain and are released from the brake imposed on them by the continued presence of morphine in the organism, thus accounting for symptoms of abstinence. This formulation seems to fit the facts. For example, morphine constricts the pupils and depresses respiratory rate in minute volume. When morphine is withdrawn, the pupils dilate and hyperpnea ensues. Many other examples could be stated. In fact, the development of counter responses which oppose the main effects of drugs may be a general pharmacological phenomenon . . . It is apparent, however, that the homeostatic theory is more descriptive than explanatory. It tells us what happens but not really how. We have very little knowledge of the mechanisms of the homeostatic responses that supposedly oppose the actions of morphine. Due to the researches of Wikler, we can describe them in neurophysiological terms. In the non-addicted chronic spinal dog, morphine enhances the extensor reflexes, and has little effect on the knee jerk. It can be inferred from these facts that morphine depresses reflexes which are mediated through multineuron arcs (the flexor) and has little effect on reflex arcs that are mediated through a single synapse (the patellar). As tolerance develops, multineuron arcs become hyperexcitable and, on withdrawal of the morphine, excitability in these arcs is unmasked and accounts for withdrawal symptoms. Similar phenomena have been observed in spinal man. It is also known that chronic decorticated dogs develop tolerance and symptoms of abstinence on withdrawal of morphine. One may infer therefore, that the cerebral cortex is not necessary for the development of physical dependence. Although these facts give us some concept of the neurophysiological changes associated with addiction we know little about the nature of the changes at levels between the cord and the cortex. Technical difficulties in studying the activity of these levels in chronically intoxicated animals have not yet been solved, but the current trend in neurophysiological research in addiction consists partly of attempts to develop such methods.

"Biochemical studies have shown that tolerance and physical dependence are not related to changes in excretion or distribution of morphine within the organism, and are also not due to any known degradation product of morphine. Eisenman and Fraser have shown that maintained addiction causes a decrease in the urinary excretion of 17-ketosteroids, 17-hydroxycorticoids, and of pituitary gonadotropin although the adrenal and the gonads remain responsive to ACTH and chronic gonadotropin. On withdrawal of morphine, excretion of 17-ketosteroids is increased, serum corticoid levels rise and eosinophile counts decrease. These results indicate depression of the adrenals, the gonads or both by morphine during maintained addiction probably because of depression of the pituitary through unknown central mechanisms. During abstinence, there is a marked adrenal discharge. These findings are very important since they explain the decreased libido and sexual activity present during opiate addiction. The psychiatric significance of this effect requires no comment.

"Efforts to elucidate the biochemical mechanisms underlying dependence and tolerance have not yet proved fruitful. Though the technical difficulties are great, studies of this sort are now being pushed. Obviously, we cannot explain all the phenomena of addiction by physiological data alone. Physiological data, though very useful in understanding symptoms

and in managing them, contribute to total understanding of the problem only insofar as correlation of physiological mechanisms with drug induced changes in behavior are possible."[30]

Whatever the mechanics of tolerance and dependence, if the addict has reached the stage of physical dependence upon a drug, he must obtain the drug regularly if he is to avoid the distressing experience of the withdrawal syndrome. How much of the drug he will use, will depend in the first instance on how much he can get. If the drug is available, despite the mechanism of tolerance, each addict eventually tends to find a level or a physical plateau in the use of the drugs. He tends to stop increasing the dosage at a point where he feels right physically and psychologically or where the drug will give him the euphoria that he is looking for. But whatever his level or plateau, the addict must obtain enough drugs to ward off the withdrawal symptoms which inevitably follow any failure to obtain the drug.

The withdrawal syndrome or sickness is no mere figment of the addict's imagination, but an illness which constitutes one of the most stereotyped syndromes in clinical medicine. Wikler has demonstrated that physical dependence is a real physiological entity and is not psychic in origin. He has distinguished the purposive from the non purposive features of the withdrawal syndrome as follows:

"The train of events which follow abrupt cessation of morphine in the tolerant addict varies within limits in different individuals, and is related to previous dosage, duration of addiction and the degree of tolerance which had been developed. However, for any given dose level and period of addiction, the morphine abstinence syndrome is remarkably reproducible in any given individual. The significance of the morphine abstinence syndrome to the individual is also highly individualized and is partly determined by particular situations. Thus, it may serve as a means for expressing hostility, expiating guilt and even justifying relapse. When observed in a hospital situation after abrupt and complete withdrawal of the drug, the fully developed morphine and abstinence syndrome is characterized by the following changes, which may be separated into two groups:

"(a) NON-PURPOSIVE. These consist of yawning, lachrymation, rhinorrhea, mydriasis, gooseflesh (piloerection) tremors, muscle twitches (particularly in the lower extremities), restlessness, hot and cold flashes, nausea, vomiting, diarrhea, anorexia, weight loss, ejaculations in men and orgasms in women, elevation of body temperature, cardiac and respiratory rates and blood pressure, leucocytosis, hemoconcentration, elevation of blood sugar and a precipitous drop in circulating eosinophile count. In addition, the subject often exhibits a rather typical facies suggestive of an individual with an acute febrile infectious disease. Often the patient 'curls up' in the lateral recumbent position with a blanket drawn over his head, preferably on a hard cold surface, such as the floor. Curiously, alpha activity in the electroencephalogram, if present in pre-withdrawal records, continues during the abstinence period in spite of manifest 'anxiety', although an increase in slow activity may be observed during abstinence following periods of addiction to other morphine-like drugs. (b) PURPOSIVE. This group of morphine abstinence changes refers to such behavior as appears to be directed toward obtaining the drug. It is expressed verbally in terms of 'craving' and demanding drugs. Also, the subject may exhibit patterns of behavior which are highly individualized—threatening suicide, or violence, assuming bizarre postures and exaggerating his distress in dramatic ways.

"The non purposive abstinence changes reach peak intensity about 48-72 hours after abrupt withdrawal of morphine and subside gradually over a period of about one week, although some physiological variables do not return to control levels for as long as six months, while the 'purposive' abstinence changes may continue indefinitely."[31]

According to Lindesmith, the necessity of avoiding withdrawal distress provides the basic explanation of the nature and the processes of drug addiction. "Addiction to opiates," he points out:

". . . is determined by the individual's reaction to the withdrawal symptoms which occur when the drug's effects are beginning to wear off, rather than upon positive euphoric effects often erroneously attributed to its continued use. More specifically, the complex of attitudes which constitute addiction is built up in the process of conscious use of the drug to alleviate or avoid withdrawal distress. This theory, though simple in form, has considerable explanatory value, and offers a means of accounting for varied and paradoxical aspects of the habit, such as the addict's claim that he feels normal under the drug's influence, as well as his tendency to increase the dose to a point where its use becomes much more unpleasant and burdensome than it need be. The hypothesis presented makes intelligible the constant preoccupation of the addict with the drug, and explains how the unpleasant and unwelcome appellation 'dope fiend' is forced upon him.[32]

"Addiction occurs only when opiates are used, to alleviate withdrawal distress, after this distress has been properly understood or interpreted, that is to say, after it has been represented to the individual in terms of the linguistic symbols and cultural patterns which have grown up around the opiate habit. If the individual fails to conceive of his distress as withdrawal distress brought about by the absence of opiates he cannot become addicted, but if he does, addiction is quickly and permanently established through further use of the drug. All of the evidence unequivocally supports this conclusion.

"This theory furnishes a simple but effective explanation, not only of the manner in which addiction becomes established, but also of the essential features of addiction behavior, those features which are found in addiction in all parts of the world and which are common to all cases."[33]

Whatever the truth of Lindesmith's theory, there can be little doubt that once a user of drugs realizes that he has become addicted his entire life becomes centered around the search for the drug. He must obtain the drug in order to be comfortable and to be able to function. He may also want the drug in order to obtain an ever elusive euphoria. The drive and compulsion for the drug is such that family, friends, property, profession may all be sacrificed to feed it. The compulsion to take the drug cannot be stopped by a threat of jail or prison sentences.

V. THE EFFECTS OF DRUG ADDICTION

The compulsion to take the drug is one of the components of the "drug fiend" myth which has been propagated by irresponsible journalism and irresponsible law enforcement. Another vital aspect to this myth is the misconception concerning what narcotic drugs do to human beings and the kind of behavior that such drugs foster. It is alleged that drugs like heroin and morphine have devastating effects on the persons who use them. Murder on the installment plan is a phrase frequently used to describe heroin addiction. It is charged, moreover, that the use of narcotic drugs leads to the commission of all kinds of serious crime, particularly crimes of violence. The printed proceedings of the House and the Senate Committees are full of such charges concerning the use of narcotic drugs. The pernicious effects of narcotic drugs on human beings were the basic justification for the severe penalties that were recommended as a means of dealing with the drug traffic and problems of drug addiction.

Unfortunately, the facts concerning the effects of such drugs as morphine and heroin on human beings differ considerably from these misconceptions. The facts tend to indicate that the use of drugs like heroin and morphine is consistent both with a reasonable state of health and with a reasonable degree of efficiency on the part of the individual user.

Over thirty years ago, Dr. Kolb pointed out that there was no evidence that the use of a narcotic drug made one less efficient. It was lack of the drug and the constant preoccupation with obtaining it which led to a loss of efficiency on the part of the individual. Thus, the drug addict is not by virtue of the fact that he takes a drug, necessarily a parasite, who is unable to function in any productive capacity. Nor is he necessarily a degenerate human being who because he takes drugs is sliding rapidly towards the grave. This is apparent from the comments of Dr. Nathan

B. Eddy, who analyzed the world literature on morphine in 1940 and who observed:

"Given an addict who is receiving morphine in amount and at intervals adequate to keep the withdrawal symptoms completely in abeyance, the deviations from normal physiological behavior are minor for the most part within the range of normal variations."[34]

Professor W. G. Karr, a biochemist of the University of Pennsylvania, wrote in a similar vein:

"The addict under his normal tolerance of morphine is medically a well man. Careful studies of all known medical tests for pathological variation indicated, with a few minor exceptions, that the addict is a well individual when receiving satisfying quantities of a drug. He responds to work in the normal manner. He is as agreeable a patient, even more so, than other hospital cases. When he is abruptly withdrawn from the drug he is most decidedly a sick individual."[35]

The feeling of normality and well being which an addict has, when he is using the drug was observable by Dr. Marie Nyswander, when she tested a group of patients at Lexington by means of Rorschach tests, both before and after using morphine. She writes:

"With the administration of morphine a striking change is observed in the Rorschach—a change which corresponds to the addict's subjective feeling that he has attained normalcy. The responses begin to fall into more normal categories; the constriction is lessened, and movement response and fantasy appear."[36]

Dr. Lawrence Kolb noted that many prominent people who led socially useful lives have been addicted to narcotic drugs, yet were able to function effectively in their business and profession.[37] As a matter of fact some who at one time were gutter alcoholics have improved themselves and their social functioning by shifting to morphine. This notion that the use of an opiate drug may actually improve the functioning of a particular individual is clearly presented by Wikler and Rasor:

"On further interrogation, the majority of such individuals explain that in ordinary life situations opiates (usually heroin or morphine) reduce appetite, pain and erotic urges of all sorts, heterosexual, homosexual or autoerotic. In addition, intravenous injection of these agents produces a transient 'thrill' akin to sexual orgasm, except that it is centered in the abdomen. After these effects have developed a sense of gratification or satisfaction is achieved and they feel more 'at ease' and free to do what they 'want to do.' In some situations they may 'want' to doze peacefully and enjoy daydreams of wealth, power or social prestige. In other situations they may want to socialize, and they feel more comfortable to the presence of women. Furthermore, some opiate users state that these agents do not impair, others state that they actually improve, their ability to do useful work and that under the influence of opiates, they are less aggressive and 'keep out of trouble.'

"It is difficult, of course, to verify statements such as these relative to the contrasting effects of drugs in actual life situations. However, observations made under experimental conditions are in substantial agreement with them. Thus, *as long as adequate amounts of opiates are administered, aggressive, antisocial behavior is practically never observed, personal hygiene is maintained, assigned reseponsibilities are* discharged satisfactorily, psychologic tests of performance reveal little or no impairment, and the sensorium remains quite clear, while anxiety associated with anticipation of pain is reduced."[38]

Opiate drugs like morphine do have certain effects upon the individual. The use of the drug causes a loss of appetite. Thus there may be a failure to maintain a proper intake of foods. This may affect health. However, as Maurer and Vogel point out:

". . . it has not been possible to demonstrate that opiate drugs in themselves actually destroy tissue or are directly the cause of tissue deterioration."[39]

The existence of emaciation and anemia in drug addicts,

". . . may be due to the unhygienic and impoverished life of the addict rather than to the direct effect of the drug."[40]

The drug addict simply does not eat enough, because on the one hand the drug he uses reduces appetite and on the other hand, costs so much that he has no money left over for food.

Another effect of drug addiction is in reducing the urge to sex.

"The reproductive system generally tends to become inactive. . . . In both males and females, opiates have a general tendency to reduce or obliterate sexual desire, although there may be individual exceptions to this."[41]

This lowering of sexual desire resulting from narcotic drugs would cause one to be skeptical of the claim that heroin and morphine incite to violent sexual crimes.

Drug addiction may result in moral and character deterioration. But here the legal and social policy concerning drug addiction may be at fault rather than the use of the drug. An addict can only obtain the drug from underworld sources. He is cut off from any legitimate supply. The underworld will supply him at a price. The price is high and most addicts do not have the kind of money necessary to feed a habit. The obvious alternative is to raise the money by theft or if the addict is a woman, by prostitution. Once the addict is started on a criminal or prostitutional career, his moral deterioration becomes almost inevitable. But the question may well be raised whether it is the drug or the short sighted social policy which utterly fails to take into account the desperate need of the addict for his drugs which causes the breakdown in character.

As Lindesmith notes:

"Addicts escape most of the alleged degenerate results of the drug if they are sufficiently well-to-do, and many addicts suffer serious 'character deterioration' only after the narcotic agents catch up with them. In other countries . . . addicts do not suffer evil effects . . . forced upon the American users. They do not steal, lie, engage in prostitution, or become derelicts to the extent that our addicts do. If the toxic effect of the drug on the central nervous system promotes degeneration, or if addiction is a bio-chemical affair, . . . why do not similar conditions result in other countries or in our own upper class?"[42]

VI. PSYCHIATRIC AND PSYCHOLOGICAL FACTORS IN DRUG ADDICTION

As we have seen, medical men have tended to regard drug addiction either as a disease or as a symptom of a disturbed or abnormal personality that requires drugs in order to be able to cope with life's problems. Drug addiction may be considered a disease if the focus of attention is the pathologic process in the human organism created by addiction. A healthy human organism does not need morphine or heroin to ward off withdrawal symptoms. The diseased body of an addict, however, requires its daily dosage of drug for the addict to be comfortable. On the other hand, drug addiction is not an accidental process. Individual factors are at work in the determination of who will and who will not become addicted, even in those areas of our cities, where the incidence of drug use is high. There are individuals who are exposed to drug use, who through an effort of will, strength of character or force of personality reject all contact with narcotic drugs. These individuals will never become drug addicts. There are also some persons who although once addicted, through will power, or force of personality and character manage to stay off drugs. It is obvious that character and personality factors are at work in the selection of addicts and in determining which addicts will relapse to the use of drugs, once they have been taken off drugs.

Who, then, are the individuals who succumb to drug addiction? What factors of personality, of character, of psychological organization or disorganization distinguish the drug addict from the non-addict? Can the phenomenon of drug addiction be explained by the disciplines of psychology and psychiatry?

Even the most casual reading of the psychiatric and psychological literature on drug addiction indicates that psychology and psychiatry are still far from satisfactory explanations as to why specific individuals take to drugs, and why others who may be similarly exposed do not take to drugs to resolve their personal problems. Over and over again, one reads that drug addiction is an expression of personality disturbance or maladjustment. An individual takes drugs to overcome the shortcomings of personality which make it difficult for him to cope with the world in which he lives. He needs drugs to enable him to deal with the anxieties and tensions arising from familial conflicts, sexual difficulties and the necessity of growing up and taking one's place in an adult society. A vast majority of drug addict patients, write Vogel, Isbell and Chapman,

". . . are fundamentally emotionally immature children like persons who have never made a proper adaptation to the problems of living."[43]

Not all drug addicts, however, fit into a single psychiatric classification or diagnosis. The personality disorders of drug addicts,

". . . run the gamut of the standard psychiatric nomenclature from the simple anxiety states to the major psychoses."[44]

Thus, all kinds of people, both normal and abnormal, become drug addicts. This can be seen from the summary by Vogel, Isbell and Chapman of the pioneering work on the classification of drug addicts done by Kolb* and Felix.**

* In 1925, Dr. Lawrence Kolb made his pioneer study of 230 drug addicts recruited from prisons, a municipal hospital, a clinic "and other addicts in good social standing in various parts of the country." This fell into the following general classifications:

1. People of normal nervous constitution necessarily or accidentally ad-

"The kinds of personality disorders which underlie drug addiction have been well described by Kolb and Felix, who list four general personality types.

"The first group is made up of normal persons accidentally addicted. It consists of patients who in the course of an illness have received drugs over an extended period of time and, following relief of their ailments, have continued the use of drugs. These persons are frequently termed 'accidental' or 'medical' addicts. Such persons are regarded by some authors

---

dicted through medication in course of illness. This group constituted 14% of the total; 9% being necessary addicts and 5% were accidental cases.

2. Care-free individuals, devoted to pleasure, seeking new excitements and sensations, and usually having some ill-defined instability of personality that often expresses itself in mild infractions of social customs. This group constituted 38% of the total.

3. Cases with definite neuroses not falling into classes 2, 4 or 5. This group constituted 13.5% of the total.

4. Habitual criminals, always psychopathic. This group constituted 13% of the total.

5. Inebriates. (Only those who had a definite history of periodic drinking with sprees were considered for this study.) This group constituted 21.5% of the total.

In 1937, Dr. Kolb and Dr. Ossenfort attempted to refine the classification in this earlier study, based upon an analysis of the first 1,750 admissions at Lexington. The addicts were classified as follows:

1. Normal individuals accidentally addicted. This group includes persons of normal nervous constitution accidentally or necessarily addicted through medication in the course of illness.

2. Psychopathic Diathesis. This group includes individuals who show psychopathic dispositions or tendencies characterized by behavior resulting from misinterpretations of environmental settings or situations, but not a well-crystalized personality defect.

3. Psychoneurosis. This group includes individuals suffering with ordinary types of psychoneurosis. '

4. Psychopathic personality without psychosis. This group is composed of persons who show deviation of personality usually expressed as con-

as constituting a special group of addicts who are different
from those persons who began the use of drugs as a result of
association with persons who were already addicted. *In our
experience, all 'medical' addicts have some fundamental emotional problem* which causes them to continue the use of drugs
beyond the period of medical need. *There is, then, no basic*

stitutional psychopathic inferiority, psychopathic personality or constitutional states, where volitional and emotional control are gravely distorted
from the normal.

5. Inebriate. This group includes individuals in whom alcoholic indulgence,
either periodic or more or less continuous, played an important role as a
precipitating factor in their addiction. They apparently have a so-called
inebriate impulse.

6. Drug addiction associated with psychosis. This group includes addicts
suffering with frank psychosis, organic, toxic or functional.

In 1939, Dr. Michael Pescor made an analysis of the personalities of 1036
addicts at Lexington, Kentucky, based upon the aforementioned psychiatric
classifications. Dr. Pescor came to the conclusion that the 1036 addicts
studied by him fell into the following:

1. Normal individuals, accidentally addicted—3.8%.
2. Psychopathic Diathesis—54.5%.
3. Psychoneurosis (ordinary type)—6.3%.
4. Inebriate—Inebriate Impulse—21.9%.
5. Psychopathic Personality Without Psychosis—11.7%.
6. Drug Addiction Associated With Psychosis—11.7%.
7. Psychosis Caused by Opiates—None.

** Dr. Robert H. Felix, in 1939, attempted to further define three
categories in the above Kolb, Ossenfort, Pescor classification, namely the
psychoneurotic, the psychopathic personality and the psychopathic diathesis.
His difficulties with these elusive categories are apparent from the following extracts of his article:

"The concept of the psychopathic-diathesis group may not be as clear
as that of the other two, but probably can best be described as a state in
which, because of some ill-defined instability of personality, no better than
a border-line adjustment is made. The individual is not fundamentally
anti-social and, with some artificial assistance, can make an acceptable adjustment. The most striking characteristic of this group is the fact that, as
a whole, they were adjusting marginally before they became acquainted

difference between 'medical' and 'non-medical' addicts except in the mode of the original contact with drugs. In persons with stable personalities, social pressure, conscience and well balanced emotional makeup negate the pleasure produced by drugs sufficiently to prevent their continued use.

"The second group consists of persons with all kinds of psychoneurotic disorders who, as Felix said, take drugs to

---

with narcotics. After their first few experiences with the drug, they felt an exhilaration and a sense of relief comparable to the solution of a difficult problem or the shaking off of a heavy responsibility. Many of them also felt an increase in efficiency which, in some cases, at least, appears to have been an actual improvement. Having once found this new world of greater happiness and efficiency, they attempted to regain it and to live therein for all time.

"This phenomenon is not so prominent in the other two groups. The psychoneurotic takes his drugs to relieve himself of whatever type of symptom he may have. The psychopath uses narcotics rather as an aggressive behavior reaction—that is, he feels a desire to be more important or prominent among his associates. He wishes to excel in deeds of daring, to be more clever than his fellows, or to stand out as an object of admiration. Under narcotics, he feels that he has more nearly accomplished these ends. As Kolb has put it, *his use of drugs is 'comparable to the compensation of little men who endeavor to lift themselves to greatness.'* In other cases, he uses this means to gain an experience of pleasure over and beyond the requirements for comfortable living. He is a hedonist. What he desires to do, he does for the pure pleasure to be derived from it. He is morally defective and hence does not consider social or ethical standards a check upon its activity. The only restraint he recognizes is painful or physical in nature. The patient with a psychopathic predisposition, however, takes his opium as a medicine which he believes—sometimes with good reason— helps him to make a more satisfactory adjustment to life as he finds it, and without which he feels inadequate to meet many of life's problems.

"The same fundamental drive, then, is present in all cases—namely, the desire to derive from life more pleasure and satisfaction, which, after all is a striving present in all mankind. The differentiations made above are probably of theoretical rather than principal importance, but it is felt that they help to clarify the problem."

relieve whatever symptoms they may have. The manifestation of the neurosis may be anxiety, an obsession or compulsion or any of the great group of psychosomatic disorders.

"The third and largest group consists of psychopathic persons, who ordinarily become addicted through contact and association with persons already addicted. They are generally emotionally undeveloped aggressive hostile persons who take drugs merely for pleasure arising from the unconscious relief of inner tension, as shown by this statement of an addict:

> I was always getting into trouble before I got on drugs—never could seem to get comfortable; I had to go somewhere and do something all the time. I was always in trouble with the law. Some fellows told me about drugs and how good they made you feel, and I tried them. From then on, I was content, as long as I had my drugs—I didn't care to do anything, but to sit around, talk to my friends occasionally, listen to the radio, and only be concerned with the problem of getting money for drugs. This I usually did by picking pockets or other such petty stuff.

"The fourth and smallest group is characterized by drug addiction with psychosis. The persons in this group, many of whom have borderline mental illness and sometimes frank mental illness, are seemingly able to make a better adjustment while taking drugs. Sometimes it is difficult to establish the diagnosis and not until drugs are withheld, does the psychosis become apparent.

"There is a category of patients not included in the aforementioned groups. Kolb originally listed these as patients with psychopathic diathesis. While it is true that some of these exhibit much of the overt behavior pattern of psychopathic persons, when studied carefully, they usually fall into a milder behavior or character disorder group, which has characteristics of both the psychoneurotic and the psychopathic groups. Included are persons with severe dependency problems, withdrawn schizoid types, emotionally immature adults, as well as those suffering with the milder degrees of maladjustment and inadaptiveness to the complications of living. Felix stated that most of the persons falling into this group were making a marginal adjustment to life before becoming acquainted with narcotics. After their first few experiences with narcotics, they felt an exhilaration and a sense of relief comparable to the solution of a difficult problem or the shaking off of a heavy responsibility. Many of them also felt an increase in efficiency which, in some cases, appeared to have been actual improvement.

"In general, persons who never have been able to make a satisfactory adjustment to life, whose adaptive patterns of behavior have been inadequate, frequently find in morphine, much as the tired business man finds in the preprandial cocktail, a means of return to 'normal.' This is a false situation which may be recognized by the tired business man but is not recognized by the drug addict. Our studies indicate that patients who have made a marginal degree of emotional adjustment to life, and then have begun to use drugs, lose some of their normal adaptive patterns of adjustment. This regression in personality represents the greatest danger of drug addiction."[45]

A consideration of the aforementioned classifications makes it obvious that none of the classifications provide specific explanations for drug addiction. Large numbers of individuals fitting into the categories of psychopathic diathesis, psychopathic personality or psychoneurosis, never take drugs as a means of resolving their personality difficulties or emotional problems. One begins to see the wisdom of Dr. Wikler's observation:

"The attractiveness of morphine for certain individuals seems to be related to some of its remarkable pharmacologic properties, namely, its effectiveness in reducing such anxiety as is associated with fear of pain, anger and sexual urges, without seriously impairing the sensorium or the effectiveness of internalized controls on behavior. The intensity of this attraction is enhanced greatly for such individuals as have been unable to gratify these needs by other means, be they 'normal,' neurotic or psychopathic . . ."

". . . the degree of attractiveness of morphine is related to 'personality structure' but not necessarily to 'neurosis' or psychopathy as such . . ."[46]

This notion that the use of opiates is a highly individualized process and is not necessarily related to mental pathology is also expressed by Gerard and Kornetsky in their study on "Adolescent Opiate Addiction." They diagnosed 30 narcotic addicts and 30 adolescent non-addicts of roughly similar background and status. The writers conclude as follows:

". . . The psychologic and psychiatric data of the study indicated that the addicts exceeded the controls in *personality malfunction to a statistically significant and clinically impressive extent.* These findings support the hypothesis that youths living in urban areas where illicit opiate use is widespread do not become addicted independently of psychiatric pathology. The data also indicate that *the converse need not be true; as youths who exhibit personality malfunction similar to that of addicts need not become addicted.* As the writers pointed out previously, becoming an opiate addict is a highly individualized process which can be understood only in the context of the individual's personality structure, past life situation and present interactions with the significant figures of his familial and peer groups."[47]

The addict as Winick points out:

". . . is responding to personality problems of great complexity. The drug addict is a person with certain personality characteristics who happens to have selected this way of coping with his problems for a variety of reasons, of which he is usually unaware. Not the least of these reasons is his access to a social group in which drug use was both practised and valued. He takes one drug rather than another because it provides satisfaction for him. Other people with exactly the same kind of personality substratum never become addicts and select other means of expression for their basic conflicts."[48]

VII. SOCIAL FACTORS IN ADDICTION

Psychopaths, psychopathic diathetics, psychoneurotics, emotionally disturbed persons, etc. would not use narcotics as a solution for their personal problems, unless such drugs were available. If such individuals happen to live in the slum areas of our cities, this offers no problem, for one of the facts of life in connection with narcotics is that illicit drugs can be purchased most readily in the slum neighborhoods of our large cities. Police officers from many different cities testified before the Congressional Committees that most drug arrests and violations of the drug laws occurred in certain limited areas of their cities, usually the areas of greatest social disorganization. In these neighborhoods live the most economically deprived groups of our population; the racial and religious minorities, and the recent immigrants into the cities. These are the areas of poor and squalid housing, of overcrowding, of a shifting disorganized family life. They are the areas with the largest number of relief cases; the highest rates of juvenile delinquency, adolescent and adult crime. They are also areas with high rates of mental disturbance and psychological abnormality.[49] It is these disorganized slum neighborhoods, whether they exist in New York, Chicago, Los Angeles, Detroit or Washington, D. C., which develop a special cultural climate which is favorable to drug use and experimentation particularly by juveniles and adolescents.

Two major studies in recent years (The N. Y. U. Study and the Chicago Study) were concerned with an analysis of the factors in such neighborhoods which were conducive to a high degree of drug use. The Chicago Study pointed out that the social environment for young males in these areas comes to be dominated by a "street corner society" and that such societies flourish in communities where the traditional influences and controls over youth tend to be weak and uncertain. The central feature of this society or culture is the support that it gives to behavior which is inconsistent with the norms of conventional society and often openly hostile to many of its expectations. This orientation on the part of the street boys is expressed in a variety of ways, particularly by delinquency and crime "and in the search for and exploitation of kicks." Success in the exploitation of "kicks" entails willingness to experiment with new drugs whose effects and properties are not precisely known to the user. However, the street corner groups appear to vary in the degree to which they court the double interest in delinquency and "kicks." There are, as an N. Y. U. study pointed out, street gangs with a high degree of narcotic use, a low degree of narcotic use and gangs which do not permit their members to use narcotics at all. Nevertheless, as the Chicago study notes, the introduction of heroin to street groups in Chicago,

". . . was facilitated by an established and pre-existing interest in the use of stimulants and intoxicants and by the tendency to experiment freely with new drugs."[50]

Heroin was "pushed" vigorously by the frenetic search of the street corner boy for newer, stranger and more status giving intoxicants, and after heroin use had been defined as "desirable and valuable by intimate associates whose views are meaningful to the potential user."

The New York University studies came to similar conclusions:

"We have learned that the social pattern of using narcotics is highly concentrated in the most deprived areas of the city; that it is associated with the type of delinquency that produces ready cash; that the pattern of using drugs spreads within the peer-group and apparently is meaningful in the context of the social reality in which the boys live; that the users (and non-using delinquents) live in a special defiant and escapist sub-culture side by side with the other sub-culture of 'squares' who want to lift themselves out of their depriving environment."[51]

Obviously not all the boys who participate in the activities of street corner society or of street gangs wind up as habitual or professional criminals or drug addicts. The wider, conventional society exercises its pressures for conformity even against the members of the delinquent and deviant sub-culture. As the boys grow older, the youthful preoccupations with delinquency, kicks, hell-raising, gang fights, etc., give way for many of the boys to a concern about the future, a steady girl, a job, a home, etc. The problem of who will and who will not become a professional criminal or a drug addict is dependent upon the personality of the individual boy. This is noted by both the Chicago and the N. Y. U. studies:

". . . Most likely to become extreme delinquents or drug users are those who by virtue of their personal histories are least responsive to the expectations of conventional society. Thus, the problem of differences between those who do and those who do not become drug addicts in the world of the street boy may be regarded as a problem of the difference in life history among individuals, with each life history constituting a unique equation of forces."[52]

"But as the group grows older, two things happen. Sport, hell-raising and gang fights become 'kid stuff' and are given up. In the normal course of events, the youthful preoccupations are replaced by more individual concerns about work, future, a 'steady' girl and the like. If most of the gang members are sufficiently healthy to face these new personal needs and societal demands and engage in the new activities appropriate for their age, the availability of drugs will not attract their interest. But for those gang members who are too disturbed emotionally to face the future as adults, the passing of adolescent hell-raising leaves emptiness, boredom, apathy and restless anxiety. In a gang where there are many such disturbed members, experimentation with drugs for 'kicks' will soon lead to frequent and, later, habitual use; cliques of users will grow quickly. Enmeshed in the patterns of activities revolving around the purchase, sale and use of drugs and the delinquent efforts to get money to meet the exorbitant cost of heroin, the young users can comfortably forget about girls, careers, status and recognition in the society at large. Their sexual drive is diminished, they maintain a sense of belonging in the limited world of the addict, they remain children forever. They may give up all sense of personal responsibility for their lives and conveniently project the blame for their shiftless existence on the 'habit'."[53]

It is obvious that in the production of a drug addict, just as in the production of a delinquent or a criminal, there is an interaction of personality and environmental factors. But there is also a shaping of personality by environmental factors, cultural attitudes, and interpersonal relationships. Nowhere is this more true than in the intimate confines of family life. The N. Y. U. group compared the family background of 30 White, Negro, and Puerto Rican families with a non addict boy and 30 such families with a boy who was an addict. All the families lived in a high drug use neighborhood. Almost all of the 30 addicts came from families where there was a disturbed relationship between the parents as evidenced by separation, divorce, overt hostility or lack of warmth and mutual interest. The addicts experienced much more frequently than the controls,

". . . cool or hostile parent figures, weak parent-child relationships, lack of clarity as to the way in which disciplinary policies were established and vague or inconsistent parental standards for the boy."[54]

As a result of these findings, this study came to the conclusion;

". . . . that the pathologic personality characteristics of the juvenile heroin addict are *consistent outgrowths of the disturbed pattern of family relationships to which he has been exposed.*"[55]

VIII. DRUG ADDICTION IN RELATION TO CRIME

One of the compelling reasons why more rational methods of dealing with drug addicts must be devised is the close relationship between drug addiction and crime. The compulsion for the drug makes every drug addict a law violator and a criminal. Mere possession of a narcotic drug which the addict must have to ward off withdrawal distress is a violation of the narcotic laws. Thus, every drug addict is subject to arrest by the police, and as we have seen, the arrests of addicts and of narcotic law violators have gone up by leaps and bounds. Addicts guilty of no other crime than illegal possession of narcotics are filling the jails, prisons and penitentiaries of the country.

However, this is only a part of the distressing picture of the relationship between narcotic addiction and criminality. For most narcotic addicts, predatory crime (larceny, shoplifting, sneak thievery, burglary, embezzlement, robbery, etc.), is a necessary way of life. This was clearly recognized by the law enforcement officials who appeared before the Congressional Committees and gave testimony concerning the close relationship between property crime and drug addiction in their communities. These officials were convinced that property crimes could be reduced materially if all drug addicts could be incarcerated.

The New York University and the Chicago studies on drug addiction support the notion that drug addiction necessarily leads to predatory crime as a way of life. For example, Chein and Rosenfeld make the following comments based on their studies of juvenile addicts:

"Drug use leads to a criminal way of life. The illegality of purchase and possession of opiates and similar drugs makes a drug user a delinquent ipso facto. The high cost of heroin, the drug generally used by juvenile users, also forces specific delinquency against property for cash returns. The average addicted youngster spends almost forty dollars a week on drugs, often as much as seventy dollars. He is too young and unskilled to be able to support his habit by his earnings. The connection between drug use and delinquency for profit has been established beyond any doubt."[56]

A Chicago study comes to a similar conclusion:

". . . Almost without exception addicts resort to theft to obtain money for the purchase of the drugs. The compulsion of the addiction itself coupled with the astronomically high cost of heroin leads the addict inescapably to crime. For the addict *there is very simply no alternative.*"[57]

There has been considerable debate as to whether the criminality of the addict preceded or is merely a consequence of the drug addiction. Studies like those of Pescor can be cited for the proposition that most narcotic addicts became delinquents and criminals *after the onset of their addiction.* Pescor found in 1943, that of the 1,036 patients at Lexington, studied by him, 75.3% had no history of delinquency prior to addiction.[58] Anslinger, however, has always taken the view that the drug addict was usually a criminal first before becoming addicted.[59]

The answer to the question of whether the addict was a delinquent or criminal prior to addiction largely depends upon the particular groups of addicts studied. For example, Kolb,[60] in 1928, studied a group of 119 so called "medical addicts," persons who became addicted to drugs as a result of the medical prescription of narcotics for ailments other than drug addiction. Kolb found that of these 119 addicts, 90 had never previously been arrested. However, the studies conducted in New York and Chicago present a different picture. These studies of drug addiction were conducted in areas with high rates of delinquency and crime. They were also concerned with youthful and adolescent offenders. The conclusion from the Chicago and New York studies is inescapable that "delinquency both preceded and followed addiction to heroin."[61]

"Persons who became users," stated the Chicago report,

"were found to have engaged in delinquency in a group-supported and habitual form either prior to their use of drugs or simultaneously with their developing interest in drugs. There was little evidence of a consistent sequence from drug use without delinquency to drug use with delinquency."[62]

Nevertheless, even in the delinquency areas of our large cities, there are persons who become addicted to drugs without a prior career of delinquency and crime. After addiction, however, they will usually turn to delinquency and crime, "often after overcoming severe psychological conflict occasioned by their repugnance to theft."[63]

Moreover, the addict who had previously been a delinquent loses all chance of shaking off habits of delinquency and crime as he grows older. Not all *non* addicted delinquents and adolescent offenders living in the delinquency areas of our large cities grow up to be habitual and professional criminals. Many abandon their delinquent and criminal pursuits when they reach early adulthood. They find jobs, marry and settle down to productive lives. But if the delinquent or adolescent offender adds narcotic addiction to his patterns of behavior,

". . . All possible future retreat from a delinquent mode of life is cut off regardless of whatever later impulses they may have to reject a criminal career in favor of a conventional one. They are constrained by their unremitting need and the high cost of heroin to continue in crime. *This interpretation supports the conclusion that drug addiction results in a large and permanent increase in the volume of crime.*"[64]

Thus, the realities of the relationship between narcotic addiction and crime appear to be much more somber than the romantic myth, "that hold-up men, murderers, rapists and other violent criminals take drugs to give them courage or stamina to go through with acts which they might not commit when not drugged."[65] Dr. Kolb has labeled this notion an "absurd fallacy." The crimes committed by opiate addicts are generally of a parasitic, predatory nonviolent character. Drug addicts may, on occasion, commit violent crimes. This is hardly surprising since so many are classified as psychopaths. A psychopath tends towards serious criminality with or without drug addiction. Generally, however, the use of opiate drugs (whatever may be the case with marihuana and cocaine) tends to discourage violent crime. As Maurer and Vogel point out:

"The sense of well-being and satisfaction with the world are so strong that, coupled with the depressant action of the drug, the individual is unlikely to commit aggressive or violent crime after he is addicted, even though he habitually or professionally did so previous to addiction. In the words of Kolb, 'Both heroin and morphine in large doses change drunken fighting psychopaths into sober, cowardly, non-aggressive idlers . . .'

". . . To date, there has been no evidence collected to show that any significant percentage of opiate addicts commit violent crimes either professionally or casually while under the influence of these drugs . . . the reduction or elimination of sexual desire tends to remove the opiate addict from the category of psychopathic sex offenders, even though he might have a tendency to commit sex crimes when not addicted . . ."[66]

Since opiate drugs do not act as a stimulant for the commission of violent crime, should not confirmed addicts have a means of obtaining such drugs legally, so that they will not have to engage in crime in order to raise the money necessary for their needs? This basic question goes to the heart of our present policy in dealing with drug addiction.

IX. METHODS OF TREATMENT OF DRUG ADDICTION

1. The Doctor and the Drug Addict

In Western Europe, and in England, the treatment of drug addiction and drug addicts is primarily a matter for the physician. (See Appendix B, appended hereto.) Physicians may prescribe drugs to addicts either in the attempt to cure them of their addiction or to keep them in a state of comfort so that they can function without fear of the dreaded withdrawal symptoms. In this country, on the other hand, the physician has largely been deprived of an appropriate role in the treatment of drug addicts. There are many who believe that the physician must be substituted for the jailer in dealing with drug addicts, before fundamental progress can be made in controlling addiction. This requires a review of the development of the laws in this country which has to a considerable degree resulted in the exclusion of doctors from the field of drug addiction.

Prior to 1915 physicians were permitted to treat addicts as they saw fit, and opiates were available to the general public. But Congress, pressured by the public's concern over the growing number of addicts in the country, enacted the Harrison Narcotic Law[67] which was designed to control the domestic manufacture, sale and distribution of narcotic drugs. The Act requires importers and manufacturers to purchase and affix stamps to all opiates and cocaine packages. In addition, importers, manufacturers, wholesalers, retailers, and doctors must register and pay a graduated tax for the use of narcotics. Narcotics can only be legally transferred under the Act by registered persons through the use of special order forms. The Act does not seek to interfere with the legitimate practices of medicine, nor with the medical treatment of addicts, for it provides that:

"Nothing contained in this chapter shall apply to the dispensing or distribution of any of the drugs . . . to a patient by a physician, dentist, or veterinary surgeon registered . . . in the course of his professional practice only."

If an addict is a patient of a doctor, narcotic drugs can be dispensed to him, if it is done in the course of the "professional practice" of the doctor. The Harrison Act did not seek to regulate the practice of medicine nor impinge upon a doctor's relationship to his patient. Nevertheless, despite the exception in favor of physicians many doctors were subjected to criminal prosecution because of the charge that their treatment of and prescription for drug addicts was not legitimate "professional practice" within the meaning of the Act. Targets of the initial prosecution were doctors who had many addict patients for whom they prescribed large amounts of drugs. Such doctors were charged with the illegal sale of narcotics in violation of the Act.

In the first Supreme Court case under the Act (*United States v. Doremus*),[68] the defendant, a doctor, had dispensed 500 one-sixth grain tablets of heroin to addicts, and was convicted of a violation of the Act. He contended that the Act was unconstitutional because it sought the control of the distribution of narcotic drugs through the device of taxing such drugs. It was contended that Congress could not constitutionally control the distribution of narcotic drugs. However, the Supreme Court, in a 5-4 decision, upheld the constitutionality of the Act, stating in the course of its opinion:

". . . the Act may not be declared unconstitutional because its effects may be to accomplish another purpose as well as the raising of revenue. If the legislation is within the taxing authority of Congress, that is sufficient to sustain it."[69]

This case did not directly pass upon the question of what a doctor may or may not do in the treatment of a drug addict. In the case of *Webb v. United States*[70] however, which came before the Court on the same day, the Narcotics Bureau was able to persuade the Supreme Court to adopt its views concerning the treatment of drug addicts by physicians. Dr. Webb had been indicted and convicted for selling at 50 cents apiece, over 4,000 prescriptions for narcotic drugs, indiscriminately to anyone, and occasionally using fictitious names on the prescriptions. It was obvious that the defendant was a mere prescription peddler, who was neither treating patients nor practising medicine. His conviction, therefore, should have been affirmed since his activity in relation to drugs was not covered by the exception in the Act in favor of physicians. The Narcotics Bureau, however, apparently wanted more from the Supreme Court than the affirmance of a conviction. It wanted an authoritative expression of opinion from the Court as to what was and what was not, *the legitimate practice of medicine in dealing with narcotic addicts.* It therefore had a question certified to the Court for its answer, which went far beyond the facts of this case and which seems to impinge upon the domain of medical practice. The certified question reads as follows:

"If a practicing and registered physician issues an order for morphine to an habitual user thereof, the order not being issued by him in the course of professional treatment in the attempted cure of the habit, *but being issued for the purpose of providing the user with morphine sufficient to keep him comfortable by maintaining his customary use,* is such order a physician's prescription under exception (b) of section 2 (of the Harrison Act)?"[71]

A majority of the Supreme Court (5-4) answered this question as follows:

"to call such an order for the use of morphine a physician's prescription would be so plain a perversion of meaning that no discussion is required."[72]

Under this decision, it became possible for the Narcotics Bureau to warn doctors against prescribing drugs to addicts for the purpose of avoiding withdrawal distress or keeping the addicts comfortable.

The position of the Narcotic Bureau was strengthened by another flagrant case the following year,[73] in which the physician had prescribed 8 to 16 drams of morphine at a time, indiscriminately to anyone, for $1 a dram. In dismissing the appeal from the conviction the Supreme Court observed:

"Manifestly the phrase 'to a patient' and 'in the course of his professional practice only' are intended to confine the immunity of a registered physician, in dispensing the narcotic drugs mentioned in the Act, strictly within the appropriate bounds of a physician's professional practice, and not to extend it to include a sale to a dealer or a distribution intended to cater to the appetite *or satisfy the craving of one addicted to the use of the drug.* A 'prescription' issued for either of the latter purposes protects neither the physician who issues it nor the dealer who knowingly accepts and fills it."[74]

In the *Behrman* Case[75] two years later, the Supreme Court began to realize that the earlier cases may have trespassed upon the domain of medical practice in attempting to dictate what a doctor could or could not do in relation to a drug addict. The Court dismissed the demurrer to the indictment of Dr. Behrman, who had prescribed 150 grains of heroin, 360 grains of morphine and 210 grains of cocaine to an addict, at one time. But it observed in the course of its opinion that:

"It may be admitted that to prescribe a single dose or even a number of doses, may not bring a physician within the penalties of the Act."[76]

It should be noted that the indictment in the aforementioned case did not allege bad faith on the part of the physician-defendant. Nevertheless the Court held that such wholesale prescribing of drugs to an addict regardless of good or bad faith of the doctor was a violation of the Act.

The aforementioned precedents enabled the Narcotics Bureau to prosecute many physicians, and unquestionably resulted in most doctors leaving the narcotic addict severely alone. However, a few physicians continued to treat and prescribe drugs for addicts. One such man was Dr. C. O. Linder,[77] who was charged with the unlawful sale to an addict "stoolie" of one tablet of morphine and three tablets of cocaine for self-administration in divided doses over a period of time. The Linder indictment, like the Behrman indictment, did not question the physician's good faith. But the Court *sustained* the demurrer to this indictment and observed:

"Obviously, direct control of medical practice in the states is beyond the power of the federal government. Incidental regulation of such practice by Congress through a taxing act cannot extend to matters plainly inappropriate and unnecessary to reasonable enforcement of a revenue measure. The enactment under consideration levies a tax, upheld by the court . . . and may regulate medical practice in the states only so far as reasonably appropriate for or merely incidental to its enforcement. *It says nothing of 'addicts' and does not undertake to prescribe methods for their medical treatment. They are diseased and proper subjects for such treatment,* and we cannot possibly conclude that a physician acted improperly or unwisely or for other than medical purposes solely because he has dispensed to one of them in the ordinary course and in good faith four small tablets of morphine or cocaine for relief of conditions incident to addiction. *What constitutes bona fide medical practice must be determined upon consideration of evidence and attending circumstances.* Mere pretense of such practice, of course, cannot legalize forbidden sales, or otherwise nullify valid provisions of the statute, or defeat such regulations as may be fairly appropriate to its enforcement within the proper limitations of a revenue measure."[78]

The Court refused to adopt the interpretation placed upon the *Webb* Case *(supra)* that no prescription to an addict which sought to keep him comfortable or ward off withdrawal distress could be justified under the Act:

"The question (in the Webb Case) specified no definite quantity of drugs, nor the time intended for their use. The narrated facts show, plainly enough, that physician and druggist conspired to sell large quantities of morphine to addicts under the guise of issuing and filling orders. The so-called prescriptions were issued without consideration of individual cases and for the quantities of the drugs which applicants desired for the continuation of customary use. *The answer thus given must not be construed as forbidding every prescription for drugs, irrespective of quantity, when designed temporarily to alleviate an addict's pains, although it may have been issued in good faith and without design to defeat the revenues.*"[79]

In commenting on the *Behrman* Case *(supra),* the Court stated:

"This opinion related to definitely alleged facts and must be so understood. The enormous quantity of drugs ordered, considered in connection with the recipient's character, without explanation, seemed enough to show prohibited sales and to exclude the idea of bona fide professional action in the ordinary course. *The opinion cannot be accepted as authority for holding that a physician who acts bona fide and according to fair medical standards, may never give an addict moderate amounts of drugs for self-administration in order to relieve conditions incident to addiction. Enforcement of the tax demands no such drastic rule, and if the Act had such scope it would certainly encounter grave constitutional difficulties.*"[80]*

Thus, the *Linder* Case lays down the rule that a doctor acting in good faith and guided by proper standards of medical practice may give an addict moderate amounts of drugs "in order to relieve conditions incident to addiction." The Harrison Act does not regulate how much a physician may or may not prescribe to an addict nor delimit either the quantity or frequency with which a physician

* In a subsequent case, *Nigro v. United States,* 276 U. S. 332 (1928), the case involved a layman who was accused of selling one ounce of morphine not in pursuance of a written order form, and he argued that the act only applied to professionals. The Court said:

"In interpreting the act, we must assume that it is a taxing measure, for otherwise, it would be no law at all. If it is a mere act for the purpose of regulating and restraining the purchase of the opiate and other drugs, it is beyond the power of Congress, and must be regarded as invalid . . . Everything in the construction of section 2 must be regarded as directed toward the collection of the taxes imposed in section 1 and the prevention of evasion by persons subject to the tax. If the words cannot be read as reasonably, serving such purposes, section 2 cannot be supported."[81]

may prescribe for an addict in his practice. This is illustrated by the case of *Boyd* v. *United States*,[82] where a physician had been convicted of unlawful sale of 30 to 48 grains of morphine, by means of prescriptions, issued to two known, confirmed addicts.

The trial court had charged the jury that:

". . . it was *not* admissible to issue prescriptions to a known addict for an amount of morphine for a greater number of doses than was sufficient for the necessity of any particular administration of it."

The Supreme Court pointed out that this statement was:

". . . ambiguous and might be regarded as meaning that it never is admissible for a physician, in treating an addict, to give him a prescription for a greater quantity than is reasonably appropriate for a single dose or administration. So understood, the statement would be plainly in conflict with what this court said in the Linder case."[83]

The rule of the *Linder* Case was also applied by the Circuit Court of Appeals of the 10th Circuit in the case of *Strader* v. *United States*.[84] There the trial judge had charged the jury that *a prescription for morphine to an addict is a violation of the law, and that it may not be given merely for the purpose of relieving pain incident to addiction.* The court in reversing the conviction stated:

"We think the court incorrectly stated the law and unduly circumscribed the testimony. The statute does not prescribe the diseases for which morphine may be supplied. Regulation 85 (of the Narcotics Bureau) issued under its provisions forbids the giving of a prescription to an addict or habitual user of narcotics, not in the course of professional treatment, but for the purpose of providing him with a sufficient quantity to keep him comfortable by maintaining his customary use. *Neither the statute nor the regulation precludes a physician from giving an addict a moderate amount of drugs in order to relieve a condition incident to addiction, if the physician acts in good faith and in accord with fair medical standards.*"[85]

Under these decisions, the exception in the Harrison Act in favor of physicians still has vitality. The Act does not purport to regulate medical practice, nor determine what drugs a physician may prescribe to an addict; nor indicate the quantity or frequency of the prescriptions. The responsibility for prescribing rests upon the physician in charge of any given case, and the courts have been clear in holding that if he acts in good faith and prescribes a narcotic drug in the course of his professional practice, he is entitled to the benefit of the exception under the Act.* As the court put it in the case of *Bush* v. *United States*:[86]

"A physician may give an addict moderate amounts of drugs for self administration, if he does so in good faith and according to fair medical standards."**

In the *Strader* Case (*supra*) the court ruled:

* In *Mitchell* v. *United States*, 3 F. 2d 516 (6th Cir., 1925) the physician was indicted for dispensing drugs unlawfully. The defense argued that no offense was alleged because the indictment did not allege that the disposition of narcotics was not made to a patient in the course of the physician's professional practice. The court held that the indictment was defective because it did not negative the exceptions specified in the act.

** The *Bush* case involved a physician who was indicted for violating the act by issuing prescriptions for morphine, varying from 10 to 16 grains, to known addicts who pretended to be suffering with painful diseases. The indictment further charged that the quantities prescribed were enough to last more than one day. The defense relied upon the rule laid down in the *Linder* case that a physician is within his rights when he prescribes morphine to an habitual user as he sees fit.

"A physician issuing morphine prescriptions in good faith to a federal narcotics agent, whom he believes to be a bona fide patient, for the purpose of curing a disease or relieving suffering would not be guilty of violating the Harrison Act."

But while the present law permits a physician to treat an addict in good faith and in the course of his professional practice, doctors are still reluctant to treat or prescribe for addict patients. A physician who treats and/or prescribes drugs for an addict patient in good faith according to medical standards will be protected from a conviction. But his good faith and adherence to medical standards can only be determined *after a trial*. The issue of whether the doctor acted in good faith and adhered to proper medical standards must be decided by a judge or a jury. If the judge or jury decide against the physician, the latter may be sent to prison or deprived of his license to practice medicine. The physician has no way of knowing *before* he attempts to treat, and/or prescribe drugs to an addict, whether his activities will be condemned or condoned. He does not have any criteria or standards to guide him in dealing with drug addicts, since what constitutes bona fide medical practice and good faith depends upon the facts and circumstances of each case. (See *Bush* Case *supra*.)

The physician's dilemma in treating drug addicts is illustrated by the case of *Teter* v. *United States*,[87] where the physician dispensed nine one-quarter grain tablets of morphine over a two week period to an addict who was used as an informer by the Narcotics Bureau. The defense argued that the indictment was insufficient because of the small amount of drugs dispensed. In sustaining the indictment, the court said:

"While the quantity was not large, nevertheless there was evidence tending to indicate that the sales were not in good faith from a physician's standpoint, and were for no other purpose than to enable this addict to further indulge her unfortunate propensities . . . Notwithstanding two other physicians testified that in the treatment of addicts, it was not improper to give them doses such as appear to have been given to the complaining witness, we are satisfied that under all the circumstances, it was for the jury to say whether or not these sales of drugs to the complaining witness were in good faith, or were solely for the purpose of pandering to the habit of a drug addict, and selling the drug."[88]*

The case of *United States* v. *Anthony*[89] crystalizes the problem which the physician faces in dealing with drug addicts. There, the defendant was approached by the City of Los Angeles to take over the treatment of addicts who

* In *Hawkins* v. *United States*, 90 F. 2d 551 (5th Cir., 1937), the physician was convicted for prescribing 15 grains of morphine to three known addicts, who he claimed were suffering from serious pulmonary conditions. The government had one witness who testified that he examined the addicts and found that none of them were suffering from such a condition. After the trial, one of these addicts died from a pulmonary condition. The defense argued that the amount prescribed was small and therefore it comes within the *Linder* Case because it was not large enough to put it within the power of the addict to sell part of the drug and thereby violate the act. The court, in sustaining the conviction, held:

". . . 15 grains of morphine was enough to present a question of fact as to the good faith of the doctor to be decided by the jury."

In *United States* v. *Brandenburg*, 155 F. 2d 110 (3rd Cir., 1946) the physician was convicted for prescribing drugs to a narcotics officer who was introduced to him by an addict "stoolie," as a "tubercular brother-in-law." The physician also prescribed drugs for the addict who claimed that he had serious gall bladder trouble and that his doctor who was out of town prescribed morphine. The defendant was treating this doctor's patients while he was away so that when the addict walked into the defendant's office, there was no reason to suspect him. Subsequently, the addict and the were former patients at the City's narcotics clinic, before it was closed. These patients were confirmed addicts who were thoroughly examined by the defendant before he prescribed drugs for them. At the trial, three doctors testified that such prescription was good professional practice. Two other doctors testified that the ambulatory treat-

---

agent received additional prescriptions. In sustaining the conviction, the court said:

"The frequency of the issuing of the prescriptions and the quantities prescribed were factors which made the question of good faith one for the jury."

In the recent case of *McBride* v. *United States*, 225 F. 2d 249 (5th Cir., 1955) an osteopath was convicted for falsifying his records and illegally dispensing codeine. The facts show that the Chief of Police of Houston, Texas, who was a personal friend of the defendant, had suffered a back injury and he was in constant pain. The defendant had given him a shot of codeine on one occasion in order to relieve a severe pain and when the Chief discovered that his pain could be relieved and that he was able to work, he asked the defendant to give him more; the defendant was reluctant to administer more of the drug because he feared the narcotics regulations. The Chief assured him that he would be within his rights if he dispensed the drug while treating him, and he brought in the regulations so that the defendant would be assured. Each time he prescribed the drug, he gave him an osteopathic treatment. The Chief had asked him not to use his name on the records which he kept because he feared losing his job if he was discovered; thus, he convinced him to use the name of an incurable cancer patient, again showing him the regulations, which he interpreted as being complied with so long as the dispensing of the drug was recorded. In sustaining the conviction, the court observed that none of the expert witnesses (4 were called by the government, one being an osteopath and two were called by the defense) would say that the dispensing of codeine in quantities given by the defendant was standard medical practice, and it further said:

"Evidence of the failure to follow standard medical practice shows a lack of good faith. So also as bearing on good faith is evidence of appellant's unorthodox attitude toward narcotics and addiction."

ment of drug addicts was not proper medical practice under any circumstances. In acquitting the defendant, the court said:

"Good faith must be determined on the basis of evidence and expert testimony. The courts cannot arbitrarily say that, irrespective of the beliefs of the physician that he is effecting a cure or properly prescribing narcotics, the amount is excessive and ipso facto a violation of the law."

"There is no dogmatic rule which the courts have laid down for the purpose of determining what is good or bad professional practice."

"Ultimately, the question to determine is not whether the judgment used was good or bad, but whether the defendant believed . . . that the treatment he administered was proper by ordinary medical standards."[90]

This state of the law offers a challenge to the medical profession. It may question the somewhat misleading Regulation No. 5, Art. 167, of the Narcotics Bureau founded on the too sweeping language of the *Webb* and *Behrman* Cases to the effect that:

". . . An order purporting to be a prescription issued to an addict or habitual user of narcotics, not in the course of professional treatment but for the purpose of providing the user with narcotics sufficient to keep him comfortable by maintaining his customary use, is not a prescription within the meaning and intent of the act; and the person filling such an order, as well as the person issuing it, may be charged with violation of the law."

Despite this regulation, *physicians may legally treat addicts. They may prescribe narcotic drugs to addicts. But they must act in good faith and according to proper medical standards.* However, the medical profession should not leave the task of determining good faith and proper medical standards to an ex post facto judgment made by twelve laymen on a jury. It should not be left to the conflicting opinions of so-called experts, who may have differing views on how to treat narcotic addiction. The profession itself, through its authoritative body, the American Medical Association, should lay down the criteria by which a physician's treatment of an addict can be judged. The A. M. A. itself should determine the standards of good faith and the limits of proper medical practice in the treatment of addicts. If the A. M. A. were to lay down standards, then the physician will know what is proper medical practice in dealing with addicts *before* he acts. A physician will also know that he need not fear criminal prosecution if he adheres to standards laid down by his profession. He will not be at the mercy of the stool pigeon and the informer. He will not tend to divorce himself entirely from the treatment of one group of unfortunate individuals, whose troubles lie legitimately within the domain of medicine. In laying down standards for the treatment of addicts, the American Medical Association may have to reconsider its resolution of 1924 condemning all "so called ambulatory methods of treating narcotic addiction."

Thus, the present law provides the framework within which the medical profession, acting through the American Medical Association, can authoritatively determine what the role of the doctor should be in the treatment of addicts and in the treatment of problems of addiction.

2. Outpatient Clinics

Medical counseling outpatient clinics for drug addicts have been set up particularly for adolescents in such cities as Chicago, Detroit and Los Angeles.[91] These clinics offer some social case work and psychotherapy as well as some medical help for the addict. None of these clinics supply drugs to their patients. These clinics were established as a result of the concern with narcotic addiction immediately after the war. They were established in various communities under pressure to do something about the narcotics problem. A clinic is cheaper and easier to operate than a hospital dedicated to the rehabilitation of drug addicts. Unfortunately, the founders of outpatient clinics were not fully aware of the difficulties involved in attempting to treat drug addicts. This awareness and understanding came as the clinic obtained actual experience. As the report of the Medical Counseling Clinic of Chicago pointed out:

"The treatment of addicts is an extremely difficult problem, in large part due to the inadequate motivation of the person and to his instability and unpredictability, which results in sudden breaks of contact with treatment and a lack of noticeable progress over a long period of time. When the individual is able to continue in treatment over a sufficiently long period, we do observe movement and progress in adjustment, both in personal and social levels. It would then seem that successful treatment of the person with a history of narcotic addiction is a very slow gradual process taking place over a long period of treatment contacts, and fraught with difficulties created by outside social and legal pressures, as well as by the extremely inadequate and weak personality that we have to deal with."[92]

One hopeful development in connection with the outpatient clinics has been the establishment of agencies where the person who has been a patient at the federal narcotics hospital at Lexington or New York City's Riverside Hospital may come for advice, counsel, guidance and help. For years, officials at the Lexington Hospital deplored the necessity of sending the released addict back to his community, where he had no one to turn to in case he needed help with his personal problems. Similarly, the officials at Riverside Hospital felt that contact must be maintained with the young addict after his discharge from this institution. A beginning has been made in New York City in providing after-care facilities for drug addicts discharged from Riverside Hospital. Similar facilities have been provided for Lexington graduates, in connection with a follow-up study of persons released from the latter institution.

The clinics serve only a small part of the drug user or drug addict population in their cities. Confirmed addicts do not willingly attend outpatient clinics if they cannot obtain drugs there. Where they do attend such clinics, it is usually under pressure of official agencies such as courts, parole or probation officers or under pressure from parents or relatives. Contacts under these circumstances are restricted and are broken off at the earliest possible opportunity.

Many persons coming to the clinics may have been helped by their contacts with these agencies. Some may have been persuaded to stay off drugs. Many addicts may have been induced, by contact with these clinics, to take the more drastic institutional treatment at Lexington. One can, however, be skeptical as to whether outpatient clinics have any kind of decisive impact on the confirmed addicts living in the communities they serve.

3. Institutional Treatment of Drug Addicts

Jail or prison is the usual method of treating drug addicts in this country. Drug addicts are incarcerated by the thousands all over the country for violations of the drug laws, or for thefts and other offenses committed in order to obtain money for drugs. Drug addicts also surrender themselves voluntarily for self incarceration under the laws providing for self commitment of drug addicts.

The only value of jail or prison for the treatment of drug addiction is that the addict may be temporarily withdrawn from drugs during the period of incarceration. Even this objective may not be achieved if the jail or prison is one into which drugs may be smuggled. There are practically no facilities for treatment of drug addicts in jails or penal institutions, beyond the forcible withdrawal of drugs. As a result, the drug addict comes out of jail or prison with his basic problems unresolved. The tensions, anxieties, pressures and personality problems which caused him to take drugs in the first instance are still with him. He usually goes back to the same environmental setting which facilitated his use of drugs in the first instance. There he also finds the same friends and acquaintances who have the same basic interest in drugs as himself. Under these circumstances, relapse to drugs is almost inevitable.

The only value of prison or jail incarceration is in diminishing the dose of heroin or morphine necessary to keep the addict comfortable. But once the addict takes his first shot or "fix," after leaving jail or prison, he starts on the inevitable treadmill of tolerance and dependence, requiring greater and greater doses to obtain the elusive euphoria. His capacity will be limited only by the amount of money that he can borrow or steal in order to obtain the drugs necessary for his physical needs. If the addict was released from prison on parole (as he may well have been) he is usually an extremely unsatisfactory parolee. No threat of reincarceration prevents an addict from continuing to use the drug. Parole officers cannot prevent continued use of the drug or association with other addicts from whom parolees can obtain drugs, when they need them.

Beyond jails and prisons and occasional addicts who may be accommodated at mental hospitals or private institutions, the only other institutional facilities for large scale treatment of drug addicts are the two federal installations at Lexington and Fort Worth, and the Riverside Hospital in New York City. These institutions were set up because of the belief that it is only possible to treat drug addicts in an institutional setting; that treatment of a drug addict is impossible unless he is first hospitalized in a drug free environment. The advocates of the hospitalization of drug addicts feel that only in a hospital setting can the addict be withdrawn from drugs and given the supportive psychological, medical, vocational and educational therapy necessary to enable him to cope with life without the use of drugs.

The author does not wish to minimize the great contributions that institutions like Lexington, Fort Worth and Riverside Hospital have made to an understanding of problems of drug addiction. Nevertheless, the limitations on the scope of their operations and their impact on the control of drug addiction in this country must be clearly understood.

The capacity of Lexington is 1280, of Fort Worth 1053. Riverside, the only narcotics hospital in New York City, is open only to adolescents under 21. It has a capacity of approximately 180.

It is obvious that these institutions of limited capacity can accommodate only a small fraction of the drug addict population of this country. Lexington and Fort Worth take federal prisoners who are drug addicts and who are permitted to serve their sentences in these institutions. No technique has yet been worked out whereby drug addicts who have offended against state laws can be committed directly to Lexington or Fort Worth. Within the limit of the capacity of these institutions such offenders may be admitted as voluntary patients at Lexington or Fort Worth for the 4-6 months believed necessary for rehabilitation. Most voluntary patients at Lexington and Fort Worth leave long before it is thought advisable that they should do so.

But even if all patients at Fort Worth or Lexington stayed for the 4-6 months believed desirable, it is unlikely that a permanent rehabilitation would result from such a stay. The programs of the institutions like Lexington, Fort Worth and Riverside are directed towards: (1) successfully withdrawing the patients from drugs; (2) building them up physically; (3) strengthening their vocational skills so that they can become productive members of the community; (4) eliminating gaps in their educational background; (5) attempting to give them understanding as to why they have had to resort to drugs in order to cope with life's problems, and (6) enabling them to resist the compulsion to use drugs as a means of resolving their difficulties.

There can be no doubt that institutions like Lexington, Fort Worth and Riverside have been a great deal more successful in the first four aspects of their program than in giving addicts a thorough understanding of why they use drugs and a resolve to resist the compulsion of drugs in the future. Addicts undoubtedly benefit considerably from their stays in Lexington, Forth Worth and Riverside. Their systems are cleared of drugs, they become physically healthier and stronger. They are taught habits of regular work and may learn some academic subjects. But the exposure of a few months to a minimum amount of psychiatry, social case work, educational and vocational activity, cannot eradicate the deep seated necessity and compulsion for drugs which most addicts seem to have. There are no magic cures at narcotics hospitals. We simply do not know enough about the processes of drug addiction to produce such cures.

The statistics on relapse to addiction after attempted cures at narcotics hospitals like Lexington, Fort Worth or Riverside tell the stark story of the basic failure of the hospital centered approach in dealing with problems of drug addiction.

X. THE RELAPSE AND REHABILITATION OF DRUG ADDICTS

One of the foundations of the present policy for dealing with narcotic addiction, which frowns upon ambulatory treatment by physicians or anyone else, is that narcotic addiction must be treated in an institutional setting. The preference for treatment of drug addiction in hospitals led to the establishment of the Lexington, Kentucky and the Fort Worth, Texas installations maintained by the federal government. It also led to the foundation of the Riverside Hospital for adolescent narcotic addicts in New York City. Those who established these institutions were undoubtedly buoyed by the hope that the institutional treatment would result in the rehabilitation of a substantial percentage of addicts. The founders of Lexington, Fort Worth and Riverside must have held the opinion that the combination of medical and psychiatric treatment, and social work, educational and vocational treatment could eliminate the curse of addiction to narcotic drugs from the patients admitted to their institutions. We have already noted the limited facilities for drug addicts provided by the aforementioned hospitals. If sound statistical studies were available on the relapse of drug addiction and they showed considerable percentages of success secured by institutional treatment, then the conclusion might well be drawn that better and more extensive hospital facilities were necessary for any rational drug control program. Unfortunately, sound, carefully conceived studies on a broad scale of the success or failure of hospital treatment of drug addicts have simply not been made. Whatever studies have been made present a somewhat discouraging picture of the possibility of preventing narcotic drug use by chronic addicts through current methods of hospital treatment.

In 1941, M. J. Pescor[93] made a follow-up study of 4,766 patients released from the Lexington narcotics institution.

He was attempting to determine the present addiction status of these former patients of Lexington. Pescor tried to obtain this information from the F. B. I. which reported the re-arrests of these patients, from their probation officers who may have had them under supervision and from the patients themselves, primarily through letters. Pescor did not make any field studies nor did he have any means for determining the truth of a report by a patient or by a probation officer, that the patient was abstinent and no longer used drugs. Thus, on the one hand, Pescor was unable to obtain replies from a considerable percentage of the patients and, on the other hand, where the reply was favorable, there was some question as to whether it was reliable. Pescor's conclusion was that the present addiction status could not be determined in 39.6% of the cases; 7% had died following release from the hospital; 39.9% relapsed to the use of drugs; and, 13.5% were reported as still abstinent. Even if we accept Pescor's figures as reliable, it is apparent that of the cases on which Pescor had data (39.9% relapsed and 13.5% abstinent), relapse had occurred in 3/4ths of the cases and *only 1/4th of the patients could be deemed cured.* More accurate tracing of the unreporting patients and more careful checking of those who reported themselves abstinent (through such devices as the use of Nallymorphine), would undoubtedly show that considerably less than 1/4th of the patients that pass through Lexington remain abstinent for any considerable period of time.

The high percentage of relapse after hospital treatment is experienced by other institutions besides Lexington. A study was made in California on 584 cases treated at the state narcotics hospital between the years 1928-1936. This study showed that only 15% of the cases could be deemed abstinent as of the date of the study and that 85% had relapsed; most of them during the 16 month parole period after release from the hospital.

In 1930, Dr. Alexander Lambert[94] reported on 318 addicts voluntarily committed to Bellevue Hospital by a City Magistrate. Of these addicts, 279 or 87% admitted prior cures as against 39 or 13% who denied any prior cures. More than half of these 279 addicts had "taken the cure" four or more times.

In 1951, Knight and Prout[95] reported on a follow up study of 75 private patients treated at the New York Hospital, Westchester Division. These were, obviously, luxury patients who could pay for hospital treatment. Data as to addiction were available on only 38 of these 75 patients. Less than half of these 38 patients (15) were reported as "abstaining" from drugs.

One might expect a considerably higher percentage of cures from an institution like Riverside, which attempts to select only promising cases for treatment and which takes only adolescent drug addicts to start with. Yet the N. Y. U.[96] study made on the post hospitalization adjustment of 30 adolescent opiate addicts is quite discouraging. Only two of the patients remained abstinent during the period of one year after discharge from the hospital. Twenty-two of the thirty patients were reinstitutionalized one year after discharge, either in a jail or in a hospital.

In the light of the data, it is obvious that more careful studies of the effect of hospital treatment of drug addicts must be made. If it is true that most chronic addicts cannot be cured by present hospital methods, this fact should be known as quickly as possible. It may necessitate the complete revision of present methods of dealing with addicts.

XI. THE SUGGESTED CLINICS FOR LEGAL NARCOTICS DISTRIBUTION

The dissatisfaction with present methods of controlling narcotic addiction has led to numerous proposals for the legal distribution of narcotic drugs to addicts. These proposals are not made by sensation seekers or by subversives who desire to undermine our society by spreading addiction to narcotic drugs. Proposals for the legalization of narcotics have been seriously advanced by conservative physicians, medical societies, lawyers, judges and responsible community groups. These individuals and organizations have been concerned with the fact that present methods condemn the addict to a life of parasitism and crime, while they also fail to control the illicit traffic or halt the spread of narcotic addiction.

Dr. Lawrence Kolb is one of many doctors who have strongly urged the legalization of narcotics under appropriate safeguards. In a recent Saturday Evening Post Article,[97] he has written as follows:

"A major move in the right direction would be to stop the false propaganda about the nature of drug addicts and present it for what it is—a health problem which needs some police measure for adequate control . . ."

"We need an increase in treatment facilities and recognition that some opiate addicts, having reached the stage they have, should be given opiates for their own welfare and the public welfare, too . . ."

". . . A workable solution would be to have the medical societies or health department appoint competent physicians to decide which patients should be carried on an opiate while being prepared for treatment and which ones should be given opiates indefinitely . . ."

"The details of a scheme of operation should be worked out by a committee of physicians and law-enforcement officers, with the physicians predominant in authority."

Other physicians and medical societies have favored the establishment of narcotic clinics, where drugs could be legally dispensed to addicts. Dr. Andrew E. Eggston of the New York State delegation submitted a resolution to the American Medical Association in 1954, which proposed that the American Medical Association go on record as favoring:

(1) The establishment of narcotics clinics under the aegis of the Federal Bureau of Narcotics.
(2) Registration and fingerprinting of narcotic addicts.
(3) Keeping of accurate records.
(4) Administering optimal doses to addicts at regular intervals at cost or free.
(5) Prevention of self-administration.
(6) Attempt cures through voluntary hospitalization, if possible.
(7) Avoidance of forcible confinement.

The New York Academy of Medicine has proposed a more detailed plan which differs in many particulars from the aforementioned Eggston resolution. The Academy proposed a six point program to stamp out drug addiction by:

1. Changing the attitudes towards the addict. He should be treated as a "sick person, not a criminal."
2. Taking the profit out of the illicit traffic by furnishing drugs to addicts at low cost under federal control.
3. Medical supervision of existing addicts with vigorous efforts towards their rehabilitation through:
   (a) persuasion
   (b) appraisal of methods of treatment and their success, and
   (c) supervision of addicts resistant to treatment.
4. Continued efforts to suppress the illicit traffic in drugs.
5. Formulation of an education program on the dangers of drugs for adults as well as adolescents.
6. Obtaining an accurate count of addicts and knowledge of the success or failure of treatment, so that epidemiology and parthenogenesis of drug addiction can be properly studied.

To implement this program, the Academy proposed that:

1. Clinics be attached to general hospitals, whether federal, municipal or voluntary, dispensing narcotics to addicts, open 24 hours daily, 7 days a week.
2. No person be given drugs at such clinic unless he is willing to enter a hospital for evaluation of his drug needs. After a medical evaluation, he should receive at

cost from the clinic the amount of the drug which he requires medically.

3. Safeguards against the addict registering in more than one clinic.

4. Drugs could be given to the addict for self-administration, but no more than two days supply would be furnished at any one time.

5. The addict be re-admitted to the hospital for re-evaluation of drug needs so that the factor of tolerance can be handled.

6. Addicts detected giving away or selling any or all of their supplies be liable to commitment to a hospital for attempted rehabilitation.

7. Current enforcement machinery be maintained to continue suppression of the illicit market in drugs.*

An interesting plan for the dispensation of drugs legally

---

* See also clinic plans advocated by Richmond County Medical Society which proposed the following:

1. Establishment of narcotic clinics in large centers where the problem is acute. Suitable private physicians can care for the occasional addict in isolated areas.

2. Fingerprinting, photographing, and registering the addict to be sure that the addict uses no more than one such facility.

3. The addict will receive his narcotics only at the clinic, hospital, or doctor's office so that he cannot resell them elsewhere.

4. Examination of the individual to determine whether or not he is actually an addict.

5. Attempt to permanently withdraw the individual from the drug.

Compare with plan advocated by Dr. Hubert S. Howe:

1. Establishing narcotic hospital facilities under federal, state or municipal auspices in cities which are centers of addiction.

2. Equipping these hospitals to examine, classify, hospitalize, and treat addicted persons on their premises for necessary periods, after which the

to chronic addicts has been formulated by the Citizens Advisory Committee to the Attorney General of California, on Crime Prevention.[98] This Committee consisting of eminent representative Californians proposed the following:

1. Upon a medical determination that a person is an addict, he shall be institutionalized for a period of at least 90 days, during which time the patient will be withdrawn from narcotics and exposed to an over-all educational and psychiatric program.

2. On release from this institutional treatment, the patient will be assisted by outpatient supervision . . . It will include psychological, sociological, economic, cultural and other elements in an effort to determine the narcotic-proneness of the individual.

3. Treatment should be on either a voluntary self-commitment basis or involuntary. The patient must be required legally to continue the treatment supervision in the outpatient clinic. This phase shall be known as Treatment supervision.

4. It is recommended that a Disposition Board be established consisting of individuals experienced in the field

---

appropriate cases would be referred to specifically commissioned physicians who would be appointed by the hospital staff.

3. Treatment of addict patients in the offices of the physicians under strict supervision of hospitals.

4. Returning patients to the hospital for final cure after achievement of an adequate social and economic adjustment.

5. Upon release from the hospital prevention of relapse through care of a commissioned physician, during the critical period when the patient is becoming adjusted to his resurgent sexual and other emotions.

of human relations who shall evaluate the disposition of cases and the duration of treatment and control.

5. If during outpatient treatment, it is ascertained by administration of Nalline or other means that the patient is again using narcotics as indicated by his withdrawal symptoms, the Disposition Board would have the responsibility of determining the further disposition of the case.

6. Should the Disposition Board conclude, after repeated failures, that the patient is "incurable," he might then be certified or registered so that thereafter, he shall receive indicated dosages of narcotic drugs from a determined governmental agency and thereby remove said addict as a potential market for criminally or illegally secured narcotics. The establishment of this phase of the program should be deferred until two years after the institution of the over-all management program.

It is obvious that various clinic plans and plans for dispensing legal drugs to addicts differ in important particulars. For example, the New York Academy plan would provide morphine to addicts for self-administration, but no more than a two day supply at a time. Other plans do not envisage furnishing drugs to addicts for self-administration because of the fear that the addict would peddle the drugs given to him and thus help create new addicts. But if an addict does not have the drug for self-administration, then he must come to a clinic or hospital to get the drug several times a day, so that he can avoid withdrawal distress. It is difficult for an addict to work on a job in any productive capacity if he must visit a clinic several times a day. To obviate this Dr. Eggston and Dr. Berger envision the use of a "depot morphine", a slow acting morphine whose effect would last at least 24 hours. Unfortunately, there is no such drug on the market today and none which has yet been devised, which does not have some rather bad side effects.

The aforementioned is an illustration of the practical difficulties which abound in all plans for the legal distribution of narcotics. The New York Academy plan envisioned hospital clinics open 24 hours a day, 7 days a week, where an addict could come and obtain his drug. This is a very expensive way of attempting to meet the needs of the addicts and would hardly find favor with hospital trustees. Other examples may be cited. The plans envisage the distribution of drugs to confirmed addicts after a study of the addict and his needs to determine whether it may be possible to rehabilitate him so that he may care to live without drugs. Unfortunately, except for hospitals like Lexington, Fort Worth and Riverside, facilities do not exist for such study. New facilities will have to be provided in communities with a large addict population. The plans are vague and indefinite as to the nature of such facilities. Moreover, the criteria for distinguishing chronic unrehabilitable addicts who must be furnished drugs in order to lead a normal life and addicts who may be reclaimed from the curse of addiction are not sufficiently precise nor are they sufficiently well known to the medical profession generally.

Any adequate hospital treatment or study program concerning addicts requires follow-up facilities in the community to assist addicts in the process of rehabilitation.

The test of rehabilitation is not whether an addict can exist without drugs in an institution, but whether he can live, function and work without drugs in the community. Before a decision can be made as to whether to supply an addict with legal drugs, he should be observed in the community, and helped in any resolve that he may have to live without drugs. Unfortunately, follow-up facilities for drug addicts do not exist at the present time. Nor do we have a blueprint as to the kind of facilities which are necessary.

An underlying assumption of all the plans is that addicts will not patronize illicit peddlers if they receive a sufficient dose of drugs to keep themselves comfortable. Unfortunately, this expectation does not sufficiently take into account the mechanism of tolerance, and the increasing need or desire for drugs on the part of the addict. None of the plans suggest how this matter of tolerance can be handled so that an addict will be satisfied with his legal supply of drugs and stay away from peddlers for additional supplies. Nor do the plans take any account of an addict's desire for drugs like cocaine, which will not be supplied by the clinic.

Finally, there is an insufficient realization in the various clinic plans that large numbers of addicts have serious personality difficulties even without the problem of drug addiction and that a mere supplying of drugs to such individuals will not solve such difficulties. A criminal psychopath drug addict is likely to continue his criminality despite the fact that he may be supplied with drugs legally. If clinics are to have success in rehabilitating drug addicts they may have to do a great deal more than merely serve as dispensaries for drugs. They obviously need social work and psychiatric facilities to deal with the personality problems of the addict. Unfortunately, even if such facilities were provided, successes in dealing with addicts are not assured. As the Council on Mental Health Report points out:

". . . Psychiatrists, experienced in managing addicts, doubt that there would be any great success in persuading addicts to undergo withdrawal and to engage in psychotherapy as long as drugs are supplied to them. A large percentage of addicts are poorly motivated for treatment. They feel that, in the drug, they have the answer to their symptoms. They do not regard themselves as being psychiatrically abnormal and, therefore, are resistant to psychotherapeutic measures. All psychiatrists are familiar with the difficulties in treating psychopaths of the kind that constitute a large proportion of addicts. It would seem unwise in the light of lack of knowledge of the etiology and treatment of character disorders for the medical profession to promise good results in managing such persons by purely medical means alone."[99]

There has been a violent opposition to the plans for legalizing the distribution of narcotics to confirmed addicts and to plans for narcotic clinics. Dr. George H. Stevenson conducted a study of drug addiction problems in Vancouver and British Columbia. He examined the arguments for and against the legal sale of narcotics and came to the conclusion that:

" . . . the proposal for legal sale of narcotics if adopted would not only fail to solve the addiction problems but would actually make them more serious than they are at present."[100]

The U. S. Senate Committee also considered the legalization of narcotics and concluded:

"The sub-committee is unalterably opposed to and rejects the clinic plan proposed for supplying narcotic addicts with free or low cost drugs. We are opposed to all types of so-called ambulatory treatment . . . Finally, we believe the thought of permanently maintaining drug addiction with 'sustaining' doses of narcotic drugs to be utterly repugnant to the moral principles inherent in our law and the character of our people."[101]

The spearhead of the opposition to legal narcotics clinics has been the present Bureau of Narcotics. For years it has opposed legal clinics and dispensaries for the treatment of drug addicts. Its main weapon against the establishment of present day clinics was the alleged failure of the approximately 44 earlier clinics,* established between 1919-1923 by state and municipal health officials throughout the country to meet a purported emergency resulting from the Supreme Court decisions which prevented doctors from prescribing for drug addicts. The author cannot enter the debate as to whether these early clinics did or did not produce detrimental results.** There is too little objective data concerning the operation of these clinics. Most of the clinics operated for too short a time for any results to be evaluated. Many of the clinics were hastily organized to meet a threatened emergency without any serious planning or precise knowledge of the problems that they were intended to meet. The ambulatory treatment aspect of these clinics evoked considerable criticism and was in part responsible for the resolution adopted by the American Medical Association in 1924, urging:

* See publication, *Narcotics Clinics In The United States*, U. S. Government Printing Office, 1955.

** See the discussion in *Report on Narcotic Addiction of the Council on Mental Health*, American Medical Association, page 3 *et seq.*

"Both Federal and State governments to put an end to all manner of so called ambulatory methods of treatment of narcotic drug addiction whether practiced by the private physician or by the so called narcotics clinic or dispensary."[102]

Incidentally, it should be noted that the condemnation of any system of treatment which places opiates in the hands of addicts for self administration is still the official policy of the American Medical Association. The Council on Mental Health of the American Medical Association reported after examining the arguments for and against narcotics clinics that:

". . . The Council does not feel that the American Medical Association should approve proposals for establishment of clinics which would dispense drugs to addicts at this time . . ."

However the Council did suggest:

". . . the possibility of devising a limited experiment which would test directly the hypothesis that clinics would eliminate the illicit traffic and reduce addiction."[103]

The author of this report tends to agree with the Council's recommendation that we should go slow in establishing narcotics clinics. He would like to see the various problems involved in the establishment of clinics carefully tested in a research setting. Clinics cannot be established on the basis of broad general principles alone. We need to know what facilities are necessary for the successful operation of any clinic. We also must be clear concerning the techniques and procedures that should be used by such clinics. Careful research and planning may make a modern clinic a success, and avoid the mistakes which bedeviled their 1920 counterparts.

XII. PROPOSALS FOR RESEARCH

It is obvious from the preceding pages that a fundamental attack on drug addiction requires some basic research. The author would like to recommend the following research projects:

1. An Outpatient Experimental Clinic for the Treatment of Drug Addicts

The Council on Mental Health of the American Medical Association has suggested, as we have seen, that a limited experiment be devised which would test directly the hypothesis that clinics would eliminate the illicit traffic and reduce drug addiction. But an experimental clinic can do more than this. It can also aid in the determination of whether it is possible to rehabilitate addicts, in a non-institutional setting, so that they can live and function without drugs. Heretofore, the opinion has been that this could not be done outside institutional walls. An experimental clinic can also try out varied techniques in the rehabilitation of addicts and decide which are most useful. Finally, an experimental clinic can resolve a basic problem in dealing with addiction; whether confirmed, unrehabilitable addicts can be transformed into productive members of the community if their drug needs are met.

The Committee should sponsor an experimental clinic

for the outpatient treatment of drug addicts with the broad objectives outlined above. The clinic should be organized in a metropolitan center like Washington, D. C., Chicago or New York, where hospital facilities can be made available for the use of the clinic. It should be restricted to dealing with only a limited number of drug addicts; one hundred may be found to be sufficient, for experimental purposes. The clinic should provide facilities for a thoroughgoing study and diagnosis of each addict. The disciplines of medicine, psychiatry, psychology, social casework and education should all be used in making such a diagnosis and study. After the diagnosis and study, the attempt should be made to take the addicts off drugs and keep them off drugs through the use of all the techniques available in the disciplines aforementioned.

For the purpose of diagnosis, study and withdrawing the addict from drugs, a short stay in a hospital may be necessary. The clinic should have access to hospital facilities for its addict patients. It is desirable that the personnel of the clinic use every device and every technique presently available to try and keep the addict patients off drugs. Success or failure in this connection can be determined through a process of periodic reporting to the clinic and periodic follow-up in the field. Besides concentrating on the drug problems of the addict, the clinic should offer psychotherapeutic guidance to the patient in dealing with his personality problems; social work help with his family difficulties; vocational guidance on how to find and keep a job; and help in overcoming his educational shortcomings. Every effort should be directed toward enabling the addict to become a productive individual without drugs.

If the clinic does not succeed in taking and keeping the addict patient off drugs after a period of intensive treatment, its personnel then should consider supplying the addict with sufficient drugs for his needs, so that he does not have to patronize the illicit peddler. The clinic will obviously have to determine what the minimum needs of the addict are for drugs. It will also have to struggle with the problem of tolerance and the demand of the addict for increasing doses of the drug. It will need to determine whether the addict is supplementing the supply of drugs from the clinic with "junk" obtained from illicit peddlers. The clinic should also continue to provide every patient with vocational, educational, social work and psychotherapeutic guidance in the effort to make him a productive individual and wean him away from drugs.

It is obvious that many coming to the clinic will need to be supplied with drugs and will be unable to function without drugs. This will give the clinic the opportunity of testing the hypothesis that an addict is in a state of apparent normality when his drug needs are satisfied, and can function productively, with relative efficiency. But can he do so in the community in which he must live, work and bring up a family, and where he is subjected to the strains and stresses of everyday living? No demonstration of the relative normality of addicts under drugs in the controlled conditions at Lexington will be as effective as a similar demonstration made by addicts whose drug needs are satisfied, yet who are able to live and function in the outside world, hold down jobs and meet their family responsibilities.

In connection with the confirmed addicts who may be

unable to function without drugs for a considerable period, the clinic will have to determine the best means of supplying such drugs to such patients with the least danger to the community. Since ambulatory treatment of drug addicts is frowned upon, the clinic may decide to dispense the drugs only on the premises of the clinic itself. In that connection, the clinic will have to determine whether an addict can hold down a job if he must come to the clinic for his supply of drugs several times daily. The clinic may also experiment with the so-called "depot morphine," if such a drug can be made available in order to obviate the necessity of repeated trips to the clinic daily. On the other hand, the clinic may decide that some form of ambulatory dispensation of drugs is a necessity in dealing with confirmed addicts. In that event, it is to be expected that the clinic will work out the best means of supplying drugs to addicts on an ambulatory basis.

It will be relatively easy to get the addict patients to attend the clinic if they are to receive drugs. It will be far more difficult to get them to attend in the earlier stage when the clinic is trying to take them off drugs. In that event, some degree of official control over the addict patients may be necessary. This may be provided by taking the addict patients from the courts of the city in which the clinic is located and working out cooperative agreements with the courts and their probation departments concerning the patients that the clinic will handle.

The experimental clinic can be envisaged as primarily a research enterprise which will provide data on the best methods of dealing with narcotic addicts outside institutional walls. Such data are indispensable for the establishment of public health clinics and will contribute greatly to their ultimate success. The experimental clinic will have to keep thorough records on what it does to and for its addict patients. Only through such records will it be possible to evaluate the possibility of success or failure in the use of specific techniques for dealing with addicts. The thorough case studies made by the clinic should also throw considerable light on causative factors in drug addiction and help in the formulation of prevention programs. It could also provide indispensable data on the procedures and techniques for dealing with addicts which could be used by the individual physician in the smaller communities which cannot support public health clinics.

In proposing the experimental clinic, the author is not unaware of the legal problems involved in supplying drugs to addicts. However, it is his belief that the operation of the experimental clinics proposed herein will not violate present federal statutes on narcotics, as interpreted by our courts. This is apparent from our discussion concerning the doctor and the drug addict. (See *supra.*) The addicts coming to the experimental clinic will be treated as patients in the effort to overcome their addiction, and will only be supplied with drugs when it is determined that such drugs are absolutely necessary to their health and well-being and their ability to function as productive individuals in the community. If they are supplied with drugs it will be in a desire to avoid the discomforts and physical difficulties arising out of addiction. The good faith of the doctors supplying the drugs can hardly be questioned within the experimental clinic setting. In our view supplying drugs to a confirmed addict in the research setting of an outpatient clinic is no more illegal than the similar supply of drugs to an addict at Lexington in connection with studies made there. Both efforts advance materially the frontiers of our medical knowledge of how to deal with the problem of addiction.

2. A Study of Relapse and Causative Factors in Addiction and Rehabilitation

We have indicated that our present social policy demands that an addict be treated only in a hospital, in a drug free environment. We have expressed doubts as to whether hospital treatment, given our present knowledge, is very effective and can effectuate many cures or rehabilitate many drug addicts. We have noted the lack of good studies of the relapse of addicts after treatment at such institutions as Lexington, Fort Worth and Riverside. The author would like to propose a thorough research study of the after careers of graduates of Lexington, Fort Worth and Riverside. A study of addicts should be made with the same thoroughness as that used by the Gluecks in their classic studies of the after careers of delinquents and criminals.[104] This will necessitate careful detective work to locate the subjects studied and thorough case work to determine what they have been doing since they left the institution in which they were originally treated.

Through such detective work and case work analysis we should be able to determine the relative effectiveness or ineffectiveness of hospital treatment. We should also be able to determine periods of abstinence and periods of relapse after leaving the institutions in which they were treated.

If a relapse study is undertaken, a thorough psychological, psychiatric and sociological study of the same addicts would be desirable. It should be able to determine why these individuals became addicted to drugs, while others who grew up with them in the same neighborhoods with roughly the same background did not become addicted. The basic concern will be causative factors in addiction based on a comparison of drug addicts and control groups. At the same time, a study of cured and rehabilitated addicts should be made in order to determine how and why men and women conquer the drug habit as well as how and why they became addicted in the first instance. Success in dealing with addiction has as much to teach us as failure. A comparison is therefore desirable of those addicts who succeeded with those who have failed.

3. Educational and Preventative Research

There is need for sound, authoritative, educational materials that could be used in campaigns for the prevention of narcotic addiction. Materials are required on both the adult as well as the adolescent level. The preparation of such materials and the planning of campaigns for the prevention of narcotic addiction will require the collaboration of the disciplines of public health, mental hygiene and education. The challenge to be met by such collaboration is not unfamiliar. It is similar to the challenges which were met and the campaigns undertaken in connection with the prevention of venereal disease, heart disease and the dissemination of better information concerning problems of mental illness and emotional disturbance.

It is the author's belief that it is possible to prevent narcotic addiction through a dissemination of knowledge concerning the nature and effects of narcotics and understanding concerning the methods whereby narcotic patterns of behavior are transmitted from one individual to another. Preventative materials on narcotics, developed by the disciplines of public health, mental hygiene, and education are particularly necessary for use in those areas of our large cities, where narcotic addiction is a common phenomenon.

Sound educational and preventative materials on narcotic addiction have not been developed largely because of the fear that the dissemination of information about narcotics would lead adolescents to experiment with drugs. It is the author's belief that ignorance is more to be feared than knowledge and that knowledge of the nature and effects of narcotic drugs would prevent experimentation rather than lead to it. As Justice Singer observed, sound education on narcotics would no more stimulate increased narcotics use "than education on fire prevention leads to more fires by stimulating people to become pyromaniacs."[105]

Prevention through education, however, is but one facet of a narcotics addiction prevention program. There is at the present time little available information on what community and neighborhood techniques are effective for preventing experimentation with drugs by juveniles and adolescents. This problem is closely related to the prevention of juvenile delinquency and crime, since many of those who experiment with narcotics engage in such anti-social activities. There are many programs for the prevention of juvenile delinquency and crime, but such programs are generally not geared to the prevention of drug addiction. The author would like to propose a research project which would attempt to formulate community preventative techniques for dealing specifically with narcotic experimentation and narcotic addiction. If sound preventative techniques could be devised and applied in our cities, they might considerably cut down the incidence of narcotics addiction.

4. Research in the Administration of Present Laws

A careful, authoritative analysis should be made of the administration of recently enacted narcotics legislation. These laws have provided increasingly severe penalties in narcotics cases. They have eliminated judicial discretion with respect to sentences. They have provided fixed minimum sentences which the judges were required to impose on convicted offenders. They have eliminated the use of probation and parole in narcotics cases, thus eliminating the possibility of controlling narcotics offenders outside prison walls.

Many believe that these changes in our laws have done more harm than good and that they have not advanced the goal of effective control over narcotic drugs. Some also feel that the new legislation has created many more problems than it solved. Accordingly, we should like to find out what has happened in the enforcement of the new state and federal narcotics statutes.

Are they providing a greater degree of control over the violation of the narcotics laws? Have they contributed to any decline in narcotics addiction? Are judges and prosecutors enforcing the laws as they are written? Are mandatory 'minimum sentences being imposed by judges or are they ignoring the provisions of the new laws in cases where they feel that statutory penalties are too severe? Has severity of sentence had any effect on convictions under the new statutes, or are the new statutes self-defeating because juries will not convict and expose offenders to severe punishments in relatively minor cases? Are the sentencing provisions of the new statutes being evaded by permitting pleas of guilty to other types of offenses which provide for lesser penalties and the possibility of probation and parole? Has the new legislation made it possible to reach the upper echelons in the illicit drug traffic or are our prisons and penitentiaries being filled by run-of-the-mill drug addicts? Have the new laws changed the relationship between state and federal law enforcement in connection with narcotics by having more cases brought into the federal courts because of the severity of federal legislation? Are state prosecutors refusing to press narcotics prosecutions because of the severity of the sentences involved?

These are a few of the many questions which should be answered by an analysis of the administration of existing narcotics laws. Such an analysis will throw considerable light on the success or failure of present narcotics legislation and the utility of our present narcotics policy. It will also serve as a fundamental guide in the formulation of the new narcotics legislation, projected by the legal research that the author recommends in the next section.

5. Legal Research

Many defects in our present narcotic laws will be disclosed by the analysis of their administration. This will require the formulation of amendments to the narcotics laws. However, the author feels that more basic legal research must be done.

At the present time the addict is treated by our statutes like a criminal. If he is found in possession of even the minutest portion of narcotics for his own use, or a hypodermic needle, he may be jailed. He may even be jailed under some state statutes because of the mere fact that he is an addict. If the addict is, as the author believes him to be, a sick, maladjusted individual driven by a compulsion, then these statutes are wrong. They must be replaced by statutes which in the first instance require the treatment of addicts and not their incarceration in jails or prisons. If such treatment is ineffective and the addict cannot be rehabilitated, the law should not prevent the addict from obtaining a legal supply of narcotics.

In the author's opinion, a new Uniform or Model Narcotics Act must be formulated, which can be recommended to the various states, and which must be based on the enlightened premises of a new social policy towards addiction. Before such a statue is formulated, a careful survey and study must be made of existing state statutes and state court decisions concerning the control of narcotic drugs and methods provided for dealing with addicts.

If a new statute concerning addiction is to be drafted, then a new look should also be taken at the problem of the non-addict peddler. Even if chronic addicts are to be given a legal supply of narcotics, the illicit peddler of narcotics must still be jailed. We should like to strengthen law enforcement in dealing with the non-addict peddler. There are many devices which can be used in this connection, some of which have already been included in particular state statutes. New devices for strengthening law enforcement can also be devised in the course of legal research.

Thus, the legal research recommended herein would have two major functions:

(1) Provide the legal framework for a new orientation in dealing with narcotic addicts.
(2) Provide the most effective controls and sanctions for dealing with drug peddlers and the illicit drug traffic.

6. The Preparation of a Volume of Readings on Narcotic Addiction

In the 1920's, Dr. Charles E. Terry and Mildred Pellens undertook a critical review of the literature on what was then called chronic opium intoxication. This work was done for a Committee on Drug Addiction, which sought answers to fundamental questions concerning the extent, etiology, nature and treatment of drug addiction. Unfortunately, as Terry and Pellens pointed out (*The Opium Problem,* xiii-xiv), such answers were generally unavailable because of the lack of unanimity of opinion on almost every phase of the drug problem.

Thirty years have elapsed since the publication of the Terry-Pellens volume. During these thirty years, a great deal of research has been done and considerable literature has appeared on problems of drug addiction. Drug addiction has been the subject of at least two nationwide Congressional investigations and innumerable state and local investigations. The material concerning drug addiction is spread through hundreds of pages of official reports, legal opinions, articles in all kinds of technical journals, publications of medical societies, the U. S. Public Health Service, Narcotics Bureau and other agencies. Particular phases of what we may know about drug addiction are found in various textbooks. Some aspects of the drug addiction problem have become clearer since the Terry-Pellens volume. Others have changed considerably since the 1920's. There still is considerable divergence of opinion and controversy over many phases of the problem of narcotic addiction.

The author believes that there would be considerable advantage in the preparation and publication of a critical selection of the materials on drug addiction which have appeared since the Terry-Pellens volume. This would help to determine the state of our knowledge of drug addiction. It would serve to illustrate and point up the various phases of the drug addiction problem in this country. The analysis of the literature would also demonstrate whether there are still any answers of fundamental questions concerning the extent, nature and effects of narcotic addiction, the social, psychological and familial factors involved, the relationship between narcotic addiction and crime, and the best methods of treating narcotic addicts. In addition the preparation of a critical volume of readings on drug addiction would help define areas where further research would be useful in helping to control the scourge of narcotic addiction.

REFERENCES

1. Subcommittee on Improvements In The Federal Criminal Code of The Committee On The Judiciary, United States Senate, Eighty-Fourth Congress. First Session On:
The Causes, Treatment, And Rehabilitation Of Drug Addicts.

Price Daniel, *Chairman*

Joseph O'Mahoney   Herman Welker
James O. Eastland   John Marshall Butler
C. Aubrey Gasque, *General Counsel*
W. Lee Speer, *Chief Investigator*

2. Subcommittee of The Committee On Ways And Means, House of Representatives, Eighty-Fourth Congress. On:
Traffic In, And Control Of, Narcotics, Barbiturates, And Amphetamines.

Hale Boggs, *Chairman*

Frank M. Karsten   John W. Byrnes
Eugene J. McCarthy   Antoni N. Sadlak
Frank Ikard   Howard H. Baker
Henry L. Giordano, *Chief Investigator*

3. Report to the House Committee on Ways and Means, from the Sub-Committee on Narcotics, May 10, 1956 (pp. 13-14).

4. Report of the Committee of the Judiciary, U. S. Senate Summary and Preliminary Findings and Recommendations—Sub-Committee on Improving the Federal Criminal Code, January 16, 1956.

5. *Ibid.* Report #1997, May 14, 1956 (p. 5).

6. *Ibid.* April 24, 1956 (p. 2).

7. Consisting of representatives of the Department of State, Defense, Health, Education and Welfare, Treasury, and Justice.

8. Report of the Interdepartmental Committee on Narcotics To The President, Washington, D. C., February, 1956 (p. 16).

9. H. Isbell and W. White, "Clinical Characteristics of Addictions," *American Journal of Medicine*, May 1, 1953 (p. 558).

10. Senate Committee Report (p. 4198).

11. *Ibid.* (p. 4624).

12. L. Kolb and A. G. DuMez, "The Prevalence And Trend Of Drug Addiction in the U. S. and Factors Influencing It," *Public Health Reports*, Reprint #924, May, 1924.

13. C. Terry and M. Pellens, *The Opium Problem*, New York: The Committee On Drug Addiction with the Bureau of Social Hygiene, Inc., 1928 (p. 48).

14. Bureau of Narcotics, *Traffic In Opium And Other Dangerous Drugs,* 1935.

15. Bureau of Narcotics, *Traffic in Opium And Other Dangerous Drugs,* 1937.

16. Op. Cit. (p. 8).

17. New York Attorney General's Survey, 1952 (p. 9).

18. See testimony Senate Committee 1441; House Committee, 9138.

19. Op. Cit. (p. 8).

20. Report on Narcotic Addiction to the Attorney General by the Citizen's Advisory Committee To The Attorney General On Crime Prevention. March 26, 1954 (p. 17).

21. Op. Cit. (p. 52).

22. Ernest S. Bishop, Medical Times, May, 1916.

23. See #13 *supra* (p. 72).

24. D. Mauer and V. Vogel, *Narcotics and Narcotics Addiction,* Springfield, Illinois: C. C. Thomas, 1954 (p. 72).

25. H. Isbell, "Trends in Research On Opiate Addiction," *Transactions and Studies of The College Of Physicians Of Philadelphia,* Vol. 24 No. 1, June, 1956.

26. H. Isbell and W. W. White, "Clinical Characteristics of Addictions," *American Journal of Medicine,* Vol. 14, No. 5, May, 1953 (p. 558).

27. See #24, *supra* (p. 20).

28. H. Kreuger, N. Eddy, and M. Sumwalt, "The Pharmacology of the Opium Alkaloids: Parts 1 and 2," *Public Health Reports,* Supplement No. 165, 1943 (p. 758).

29. *Ibid.* (p. 808).

30. Op. Cit. (pp. 5-6).

31. A. Wikler, *Opiate Addiction,* Springfield, Illinois: C. C. Thomas, 1953 (pp. 36-37).

32. A. Lindesmith, *Opiate Addiction,* Evanston, Illinois: Principia Press, 1947 (pp. 87-88).

33. *Ibid.* (p. 165).

34. Op. Cit. (p. 729).

35. Documentation of the Fifth Annual Conference of Committees of the World Narcotic Defense Association and International Narcotic Education Association, New York, 1932.

36. M. Nyswander, *The Drug Addict As A Patient,* New York: Grune & Stratton, 1956 (p. 61).

37. L. Kolb, "Drug Addiction As A Public Health Menace," *Scientific Monthly,* May, 1939 (p. 4).

38. A. Wikler and R. Rasor, Psychiatric Aspects of Drug Addiction, *American Journal of Medicine*, Vol. 14, No. 5, May, 1953 (pp. 567-568).

39. Op. Cit. (p. 67).

40. See #28, *supra* (p. 729).

41. See #24, *supra* (p. 68).

42. Op. Cit. (p. 41).

43. V. Vogel, H. Isbell, and K. Chapman, "Present Status of Narcotic Addiction," *Journal of American Medical Association*, Vol. 138, December 4, 1948 (p. 1997).

44. *Ibid*.

45. *Ibid*. (pp. 1997-1999).

46. See #31, *supra* (p. 54).

47. D. Gerard and C. Kornetsky, *Adolescent Opiate Addiction: A Study Of Control And Addict Subjects*, Research Center For Human Relations New York University, 1955.

48. C. Winick, "Narcotics Addiction And Its Treatment," *Law And Contemporary Problems*, Duke University School of Law, Vol. 22, W. 1957 (pp. 9-34).

49. See, for example, R. E. Faris and H. W. Dunham, *Mental Disorders In Urban Areas*, Chicago, 1939.

50. Illinois Institute for Juvenile Research and Chicago Area Project, *Drug Addiction Among Young Persons In Chicago*, October, 1953.

51. Research Center for Human Relations, New York University, *Studies On Narcotics Use Among Juveniles*, September, 1955 (p. 12).

52. See #50, *supra* (p. 16).

53. Research Center for Human Relations, New York University, *Heroin Use and Street Gangs*, March, 1956 (pp. 12-13).

54. Research Center for Human Relations, New York University, *Family Background As An Etiologic Factor In Personality Predisposition To Heroin Addiction*, 1956 (p. 8).

55. *Ibid*. (p. 9).

56. *Law & Contemporary Problems*, Duke University School of Law, Vol. 22, No. 1, 1957 (pp. 53-54).

57. Special Report on Heroin Addiction in Chicago, 1957 (p. 43).

58. M. Pescor, "A Study Of Drug Addicts," *Public Health Reports*, Supplement No. 143, 1943.

59. H. J. Anslinger and W. F. Tompkins, *The Traffic in Narcotics*, New York: Funk & Wagnalls Co., 1953 (p. 170).

60. L. Kolb, "Drug Addiction, A Study Of Some Medical Cases," *Archives of Neurology and Psychiatry, Vol.* 20, 1928 (pp. 171-183).

61. See #50, *supra* (p. 6).
62. See #57, *supra*.
63. *Ibid.*
64. *Ibid.* (p. 44).
65. See #24, *supra* (p. 211).
66. *Ibid.* (pp. 216-217).
67. 38 Stat. 785 (1914), 26 U. S. C. 2550 (1939), 26 U. S. C. 4701 (1954).
68. 249 U. S. 86 (1919).
69. *Ibid.* (p. 94).
70. 249 U. S. 96 (1919).
71. (Italics mine).
72. 249 U. S. 96, 100.
73. *Jin Fuey Moy* v. *United States,* 254 U. S. 189 (1920).
74. *Ibid.* (p. 194) (Italics mine).
75. *United States* v. *Behrman,* 258 U. S. 280 (1922).
76. *Ibid.* (p. 289).
77. *United States* v. *Linder,* 268 U. S. 5 (1925).
78. *Ibid.* (p. 18) (Italics mine).
79. *Ibid.* (p. 20) (Italics mine).
80. *Ibid.* (p. 22) (Italics mine).
81. 276 U. S. 332, 342 (1928).
82. 271 U. S. 104 (1926).
83. 271 U. S. 104, 107 (1926).
84. 72 F. 2d 589 (10th Cir., 1934).
85. *Ibid.* (p. 591) (Italics mine).
86. 16 F. 2d 709 (5th Cir., 1927).
87. 12 F. 2d 224 (7th Cir., 1926).
88. *Ibid.* (p. 225).
89. 15 F. Supp. 553, Dist. Ct., S. D. Calif. (1936).
90. *Ibid.* (p. 560).
91. Department of Public Health, Illinois, *Medical Counselling For Drug Addicts,* 1953.
92. *Ibid.* (p. 73).
93. M. J. Pescor, "Follow-Up Study of Treated Narcotic Drug Addicts," *Public Health Reports,* Supplement No. 170, 1943 (pp. 1-18).
94. A. Lambert, "Narcotic Addiction, Report Of The Mayor's Committee To Honorable Richard C. Patterson, Jr., Commissioner Of Correction," *Journal Of American Medical Association,* Vol. 93, October 26, 1929 (pp. 1297-1301).
95. R. Knight and C. Prout, "A Study Of Results in Hospital Treat-

ment of Drug Addictions," *American Journal of Psychiatry*, Vol. 108, 1951 (p. 303).

96. Research Center for Human Relations, New York University, *Post-Hospitalization Adjustment: A Follow-Up Study Of Adolescent Opiate Addicts*, October, 1956 (p. 48).

97. L. Kolb, "Let's Stop This Narcotic Hysteria," *Saturday Evening Post*, 229: July 28, 1956.

98. See #20, *supra* (p. 40).

99. Report of the Council on Mental Health, of the American Medical Association, on *Narcotic Addiction* (p. 36).

100. G. H. Stevenson, "Arguments For And Against The Legal Sale of Narcotics," *Bulletin of the Vancouver Medical Association*, Vol. 31, No. 4.

101. Op. Cit.

102. See #99, *supra* (pp. 7-8).

103. *Ibid.* (p. 48).

104. Sheldon and Eleanor Glueck, *500 Criminal Careers; 1,000 Juvenile Delinquents; 500 Delinquent Women; Unravelling Juvenile Delinquency.*

105. Senate Report (p. 880).

APPENDIX B

An Appraisal of International, British and Selected European Narcotic Drug Laws, Regulations and Policies

by RUFUS KING

In canvassing existing sources and planning its own studies, the Joint Committee of the American Bar Association and the American Medical Association on Narcotic Drugs had necessarily to inquire about the workings of comparable narcotic drug control systems in other parts of the world. It quickly developed that American authorities are in conflict about other systems; especially with respect to the situation in Great Britain there is disagreement even as to whether a so-called narcotics problem exists on any significant scale.

It was therefore decided to make some of the resources provided by the Russell Sage Foundation available to permit observations at first hand (facilitated by the fact that a Joint Committee member was already committed to be in Europe in connection with Bar Association activities). The conclusions which follow are thus supported by direct study and interviews with public officials and others in the United Nations headquarters in New York and Geneva, and in England, Scotland, Denmark, Norway, Sweden, Belgium and Italy. No effort has been made to appraise conditions in areas other than the United Kingdom and Western Europe because analogies with nations which produce drugs domestically on an extensive scale, or whose political and cultural patterns differ widely from our own, seem sharply limited in value as guidance for the Joint Committee.

The conclusions reached in this study are two: first, efforts to control drugs by international prohibition measures, though desirable and successful in part, are unlikely to be a major factor in solving our domestic addiction problem within the United States; and second, the experience of comparable national communities in Europe in recent years has been startlingly different from our own with respect to the drug addiction problem, owing largely to a difference in their attitudes and enforcement policies regarding addicted persons and the medical profession.

INTERNATIONAL TREATIES AND AGREEMENTS

No one sensitive to the deplorable part our forebears played in the Opium Wars and the commercial exploitation of the traffic in smoking opium in the Far East can wholly deprecate international efforts to suppress the drug traffic. Early in this century the United States gave vigorous leadership to a world-wide movement to stamp out opium smoking. President Theodore Roosevelt initiated the discussions which led to the Hague Opium Convention of 1912[1] (and our own Congress had been attempting to stamp out American participation in the traffic since the first Opium Tax Act of 1890).[2] Opium smoking and the illicit traffic in crude opium are no longer a problem of significance except domestically in national communities where the poppy is still cultivated.

But, perhaps because of this success, the United States has also remained a vigorous supporter of international efforts to prohibit trafficking in manufactured drugs (morphine, heroin, etc.) as well. And here its leadership has been less universally acknowledged. Because the raw materials of drug manufacture are not produced in this country and manufacture is relatively easy to control, our illicit traffic has always been fed almost exclusively by smuggling activities. Thus if all other nations could be induced to agree to curb manufacture, export, and uncontrolled trafficking in the drugs which feed our illicit market, our problem would be solved.

The extent to which American spokesmen have continued to dominate the international scene in this field is impressive. Our representatives have always been principally identified with the activities of the narcotic drug section of the League of Nations and its Opium Advisory Committee. Our Federal Narcotic Bureau has never lost its close connections with the work of the League and its successor organization, the Commission on Narcotic Drugs of the United Nations Economic and Social Council. Today the U. S. Commissioner of Narcotics serves as Chairman of the fifteen-member UN Commission.

The 1912 Convention, besides committing its signatories to impose limits and controls on the production, manufacture and distribution of opium and coca products, bound them to enact national laws curbing the export of drugs to illicit foreign markets. There have been eight international agreements since: the Geneva Convention of 1925,[3] attempting to set up a production quota system and establishing the Permanent Central Opium Board to administer it; the Geneva Opium Agreement of 1925,[4] binding the principal Asiatic producers of opium to establish government monopolies for easier control; the Geneva Convention of 1931,[5] extending the limitations on manufacture and distribution of drugs and creating an international Drug Supervisory Body to police them; the Bangkok Agreement of 1931,[6] calling for government monopolies of the retail sale of opium in Asiatic countries; the 1936 Convention[7] (with less than a score of adherents), establishing direct criminal sanctions to punish trafficking; the Protocol of 1946,[8] bringing all prior Conventions under the supervision of the United Nations and establishing the UN Commission; the Protocol of 1948,[9] providing machinery for the addition of new drugs to the controlled categories by action of the World Health Organization; and the Protocol of 1953[10] (with only a handful of adherents), agreeing to limitations on the cultivation of poppies.

The UN Commission has now under way a project for combining all of the foregoing agreements into one Convention, though this work appears to be proceeding slowly and to be encountering resistance.

It is sometimes charged that Communist countries, particularly Red China,[11] actively engage in fostering our domestic traffic in illicit drugs, but there is no substantial evidence that this is done—at least not as a matter of national policy—by any nation. Large producers of opium in the East and Near East are unwilling to repress lucrative industries, and most nations which have no serious problem within their own borders tend to be apathetic.

Of course it must be conceded that if all the existing international agreements were universally adhered to and vigorously enforced, they would have a marked effect on the flow of smuggled drugs into the United States. Our domestic problem responded remarkably to the isolation and interruptions of foreign commerce which characterized the period of World War II. But even full cooperation among nations would be unlikely wholly to eradicate addiction; and the goal of effective collective action appears to be unattainable under existing circumstances.

The conclusion that drug addiction within the United States cannot be effectively controlled through international cooperation does not, of course, entirely negative the value of such activities as the exchange of information, the pooling of resources at administrative and police levels to control drug shipments and combat smuggling, or even efforts to impose limitations on raw material production. The problem is merely one of balancing perspective; far less than a full solution for our problem is likely ever to be found in prohibitory activities at the international level.

GREAT BRITAIN

The British experience in controlling drug addiction has become a subject of controversy in the United States. The Federal Bureau of Narcotics insists that the English have an illicit drug traffic of the same magnitude and viciousness as our own, and that the enforcement policies of the two countries are identical.[12] Since 1954 the Bureau has been circulating a document entitled, "British Narcotic System"[13] which asserts:

"Several years ago a professor of sociology[14] at an American university . . . wrote an article in which he advocated that the United States adopt the British system of handling drug addicts by having doctors write prescriptions for addicts. He reported that this system had abolished the black market in narcotics and that consequently there were only 326 drug addicts in the United Kingdom. . . .

"Nothing could be further from the truth. The British system is the same as the United States system. The following is an excerpt of a letter dated July 18, 1953, from the British Home Office, concerning the prescribing of narcotic drugs by the medical profession:

" 'A doctor may not have or use the drugs for any other purpose than that of ministering to the strictly medical needs of his patients. The continued supply of drugs to a patient either direct or by prescription, solely for the gratification of addiction is not regarded as a medical need.' . . .

"The British Government is a party to all of the international narcotic conventions to which the United States is a party. They enforce treaties in the same manner as the United States.

The British and United States systems for enforcing narcotic laws are exactly the same."

Giving full weight to such disparity of views, it is nonetheless stated here without hesitation that England (and the U. K. countries which follow her pattern) has no significant drug-addiction problem, no organized illicit trafficking, and no drug-law enforcement activities that could be regarded as comparable to those which preoccupy our own authorities.

The key to this difference appears to be that the British medical profession is in full and virtually unchallenged control of the distribution of drugs, and this includes distribution, by prescription or administration, to addicts when necessary. The police function is to aid and protect medical control, rather than to substitute for it.

Some of the distinctions are subtle. Discrepancies between British form and British substance, in the endearing tradition of "muddling through," make it possible to focus upon statements, like that quoted from the Home Office letter in the document referred to above, which are true and yet misleading apart from their qualifying context— *i.e.,* in the instant case, doctors include the imminence of withdrawal symptoms among the "strictly medical needs" of their patients, and ministering to an addict under the conditions which will be discussed below is not regarded by either the profession or the authorities as "solely for the gratification of addiction." The controlling fact is that the medical profession accepts and treats addicts as patients so that virtually none are driven to support a black market; the prime corollary is that if all curative efforts fail the incurable addict may still be provided for on a

medically-supervised regime; and the remarkable consequence is that the number of persons in the incurable or
extended-regime category—out of Britain's population of
over fifty millions—remains year after year *in the range
between three and four hundred.* At the end of 1956 the
figure was 333.

It is of interest that around one hundred of these chronic
cases are from the ranks of the medical profession itself
(75,000 doctors, plus nurses, hospital staffs, technicians,
and persons in related careers). British authorities con-
cede that some persons—scores, perhaps—may be obtaining and using narcotics by some personal arrangement
which makes it unnecessary for them to appear on the
Home Office list. But the list is inclusive, with only this
minimal degree of probable error.[15] It does not include
persons whose addiction has been medically induced, *i.e.,*
terminal cancer patients and other chronic sufferers; another list of addicted persons in this category averages
about the same length, remaining at less than four hundred.

The British first imposed controls on narcotic drugs in
the same period (1920)[16] when our enforcement policies
were being developed under the Harrison Act. Their regulatory pattern is very similar to ours:[17] everyone who has
occasion to handle "dangerous drugs" must register, obtain
a license, and keep accurate records. With respect to distribution,[18] pharmacists must preserve prescriptions and
record all sales, and pharmacists' records are inspected
periodically by local police officers (who also keep an eye
on the distribution of other substances in the dangerous
drug and poison categories). Pharmacists are thus watched
with some care. The requirement that doctors keep records,

however, is not vigorously enforced, but if a doctor's practice in the matter is questioned, or if the prescription records show him to be prescribing unusual amounts, he may be approached by a medical inspector from the Ministry of Health, though he would never be called to account by the police agencies.[19]

The Act now provides maximum penalties of one thousand pounds' fine and ten years' imprisonment,[20] though such penalties are not meted out in practice. The usual kinds of offense are petty defections like the forgery of personal prescriptions, or the practice of deception by an addict's representing himself to be in need of treatment simultaneously to more than one doctor. It is of interest that the latter offense is cast by the regulations solely in terms of the deception practiced on the second prescriber, so the doctors themselves cannot become implicated. The offense of unauthorized possession is qualified as follows:[21]

"Provided that a person supplied with a drug or preparation by, or upon a prescription given by, a medical practitioner shall not be deemed to be a person generally authorized to be in possession of the drug or preparation if he was then being supplied with a drug or preparation by, or on a prescription given by, another medical practitioner in the course of treatment, and did not disclose the fact to the first-mentioned medical practitioner before the supply by him or on his prescription."

In 1956, sentences for offenses involving opium ranged from 2 months to 6 months and fines from £5 to £100; for marihuana offenses, from 6 weeks to 5 years and from £2 to £250; and for manufactured drug offenses (heroin, morphine, etc.), from 1 day to 6 months and 10s. to £100.[22]

Addiction among doctors is a comparatively serious problem, as has been noted, but the sanction applied in such cases is loss of authority to prescribe narcotic drugs under the Dangerous Drugs Act, and not loss of authority to practice medicine. If an addicted doctor puts himself under the care of another doctor, he is not likely to encounter any sanctions or difficulties.

The first regulations under the Dangerous Drug Act of 1920 actually left unsettled the same ambiguity which has given so much trouble in interpreting the Harrison Act: whether the treatment of addicted persons is bona fide medical practice or not. They merely exempted classes of persons from the ban on possession in the following general language:

"Subject to the provisions of these Regulations a person who is a member of any of the following classes, that is to say:

(a) duly qualified medical practitioners;

(b) . . .

shall be authorised, so far as may be necessary for the practice or exercise of his said profession, function or employment, and in his capacity as a member of his said class, to be in possession of and to supply drugs."[23]

Paralleling the course of development in the United States even further, the Home Office early took a narrow view of this exemption. Its ruling—still set forth as a guide for practitioners[24] and hence still properly cited as in the letter referred to by the Narcotics Bureau (*supra*, p. 126) was as follows:

"7. The authority granted to a doctor or dentist to possess and supply dangerous drugs is limited by the words *so far as may* *be necessary for the practice or exercise of his profession.* In no circumstances may dangerous drugs be used for any other purpose than that of ministering to the strictly medical or dental needs of his patients. The continued supply of dangerous drugs to a patient solely for the gratification of addiction is not regarded as 'medical need'. In a number of cases doctors and dentists who have obtained drugs ostensibly for the needs of their practices and have subsequently diverted them to the gratification of their own addiction have been convicted of offenses under the Dangerous Drugs Act."*

Here, however, the parallel ended, for after several years of confusion, while the Home Office refrained from prosecutions based on bona fide ministrations to addicts in view of the ambiguity of the law and regulations, the British medical profession took matters into its own hands. In 1926 the Rolleston Committee, a committee of eminent doctors appointed by the Government to advise on the point, concluded that providing addicted drug users with drugs under suitable controls was distinguishable from supplying "solely for the gratification of addiction,"[25] and set forth the following guiding precepts:

"Precautions to be Observed in the Administration of Morphine or Heroin.

The position of a practitioner when using morphine or heroin in the treatment of persons who suffer from addiction to either of these drugs obviously differs in several important respects from that in which he is placed when using the drug in the ordinary course of his medical practice for the treatment of persons not so affected. Not only will the objects of treatment usually differ but also the dangers to be avoided, and the pre-

---

* Emphasis in original.

cautions that are therefore necessary. It is thus convenient to discuss these precautions separately as regards:

(i) The administration of the drugs to persons who are already victims of addiction, and

(ii) The ordinary use of the drugs in medical and surgical practice.

"In the preceding section, the conclusion has been stated that morphine or heroin may properly be administered to addicts in the following circumstances, namely, (a) where patients are under treatment by the gradual withdrawal method with a view to cure, (b) where it has been demonstrated, after a prolonged attempt at cure, that the use of the drug cannot be safely discontinued entirely on account of the severity of the withdrawal symptoms produced, (c) where it has been similarly demonstrated that the patient, while capable of leading a useful and relatively normal life when a certain minimum dose is regularly administered, becomes incapable of this when the drug is entirely discontinued.

"Precautions in the Treatment of Addicts by the Gradual Withdrawal Method.

In these cases the primary object of the treatment is the cure of the addiction, if practicable. The best hope of cure being afforded by treatment in a suitable institution or nursing home, the patient should, if possible, be induced to enter such an institution or home. If he is unable, or refuses to adopt this course, the practitioner must attempt to cure his condition by steady, judicious reduction of the dose. The general lines of the treatment, as carried out by the practitioners of special experience, have already been described. For success it is necessary that the patient should be seen frequently, be under sufficient control, and be in the care of a capable and reliable nurse. The practitioner should endeavour to gain his patient's confidence, and to induce him to adhere strictly to the course of treatment prescribed, especially as regards the amount of the drug of addiction which is taken. This last condition is particularly difficult to secure, as such patients are essentially unreliable and will not infrequently endeavour to obtain supplementary supplies of the drug. If, however, the practitioner finds that he cannot maintain the necessary control of the patient, he must consider whether he can properly continue indefinitely to bear the sole responsibility for the treatment.

"When the practitioner finds that he has lost control of the patient, or when the course of the case forces him to doubt whether the administration of the drug can, in the best interests of the patient, be completely discontinued, it will become necessary to consider whether he ought to remain in charge of the case, and accept the responsibility of supplying or ordering indefinitely the drug of addiction in the minimum doses which seem necessary. The responsibility of making such a decision is obviously onerous, and both on this ground, and also for his own protection, in view of the possible inquiries by the Home Office which such continuous administration may occasion, the practitioner will be well advised to obtain a second opinion on the case.

"Precautions in Treatment of Apparently Incurable Cases.

These will include both the cases in which the severity of withdrawal symptoms, observed on complete discontinuance after prolonged attempted cure, and the cases in which the inability of the patient to lead, without a minimum dose, a relatively normal life appear to justify continuous administration of the drug indefinitely. They may be either cases of persons whom the practitioner has himself already treated with a view to cure, or cases of persons as to whom he is satisfied, by information received from those by whom they have been previously treated, that they must be regarded as incurable. In all such cases the main object must be to keep the supply of the drug within the limits of what is strictly necessary. The practitioner must, therefore, see the patient sufficiently often to maintain such observation of his condition as is necessary for justifying the treatment. The opinion expressed by witnesses was to the effect that such patients should ordinarily be seen not less frequently than once a week. The amount of the drug supplied or ordered on one occasion should not be more than is sufficient to last until the next time the patient is to be seen. A larger supply would only be justified in exceptional cases, for example (on a sea voyage), when the patient was going away in circumstances in which he would not be able to obtain medical advice. In all other cases he should be advised to place himself under the care of another practitioner, who should be placed in communication with his previous medical adviser in order that he might be informed as to the nature of the case and the course of treatment which was being pursued.

"A practitioner when consulted by a patient not previously under his care, who asks that morphine or heroin may be administered or ordered for him for the relief of pain or other symptoms alleged to be urgent, should not supply or order the drug unless satisfied as to the urgency, and should not administer or order more than is immediately necessary. If further administration is desired, in a case in which there is no organic disease justifying such administration, the request should not be acceded to until after the practitioner has obtained from the previous medical attendant an account of the nature of the case. Requests from one practitioner to another for such information should obviously receive immediate attention."

Thus it came to be recognized and established many years ago that the addict in British society remained the addict-patient; he never became, as in ours, the addict-criminal. The precepts just quoted, from the Rolleston Report, have been printed ever since as an appendix to the Home Office Instructions on the Duties, etc. of doctors under the Act.[26]

The official attitude is well summarized in the Government's current report to the U. N. Commission:[27]

"There is no compulsory treatment of drug addicts in the United Kingdom. . . . In the United Kingdom the treatment of a patient is considered to be a matter for the doctor concerned. The nature of the treatment given varies with the circumstances of each case."

Nor is it as illogical as might appear at first blush to leave the Home Office statement and Sir Humphrey Rolleston's in juxtaposition in the current regulatory instructions. Lurking behind all regulatory efforts in the 'twenties was the spectre of the "script doctor," the truly unethical practitioner who abused his license to fill the role, in effect, of our detested dope peddler. If he appeared in England, and did not yield to the gentle suasions of his professional confreres and the civil authorities, it is safe to surmise that he might have been—and could still be—vigorously prosecuted as a grave offender against the Act and Regulations.

The British medical profession has remained, with the inevitable occasional exception, very responsible in the application of the foregoing principles. The primary aim of treatment is to cure the patient by freeing him from his affliction if possible, precisely as in other branches of therapy. Consultation and the concurrence of a second medical opinion are sought as a matter of course before an addicted person is put on any kind of permanent regime. Great care is ordinarily taken to examine and probe into the condition and history of any new patient who claims a history of addiction. And doctors cooperate informally with the Home Office by reporting addicts under treatment to the Dangerous Drugs Division.

The last mentioned cooperation by the medical profession is, of course, supplemented by the reports of the police inspectors who check pharmacists' registers from time to time. Addicts who are receiving a steady supply of narcotic drugs will be revealed by this check, as well as those who falsify prescriptions or are receiving double dosages by practising fraud—the offense at which police activities are primarily aimed. The number of addicts presently known to the authorities by virtue of this double check, less than 400 in the non-medical category, as has been noted, hence seems quite likely to be a reliable measure.

Enforcement officials in the Home Office say that there is simply no illicit trafficking in the opiates; that no drugs of British manufacture have ever been identified in seizures in the illicit markets of other countries; and that new addicts usually become known to the authorities within six months. The possibility of some epidemic-like change in the pattern is recognized (as has been observed, on a minute scale, in the use of marihuana); but the situation has remained stable for many years and there are no present indications to suggest any significant growth in the addict population.

In 1956 the Minister of Health, allegedly responding to

pressure from the United States, announced that he proposed to ban the use of heroin in Great Britain for medical purposes. Following this announcement medical practitioners began to buy up supplies,[28] prices rose, and it is believed that a small black market may have made its appearance. Some prominent doctors thereupon organized a campaign to oppose the ban, prevailing upon the Minister, after a much-publicized controversy, to prohibit only the exportation of the drug. Thus the Minister "saved face" while leaving the profession free in the matter. There is still mild resentment over the fact that because heroin was removed from the British Pharmacopeia in 1956 when the ban was proposed, American authorities hailed this as a prohibition and still make statements to the effect that England has joined the United States in outlawing the drug.

Home Office officials believe that even if they stopped all lawful importation of opiates for all purposes, the problem of addiction would remain because addicted persons would be compelled to sustain their condition by the development of a black market. They complain that most of the publicity and press comments about drug problems in the United Kingdom are not authoritative. It was suggested that some of the addicts who have run afoul of the law (or who may be importing their own drugs) are simply unaware of the true state of affairs and of the fact that they can obtain relief and assistance from the medical profession merely by application to a doctor.

The foregoing general and statistical observations were confirmed in a study of local conditions in Glasgow and Edinburgh. In Glasgow, with a population of 1.25 million, four officers of the police department are assigned to enforcement of the regulatory provisions of the Dangerous Drug Act, devoting their full time to inspecting pharmacies, checking records, and investigating alleged violations and abuse. These men are wholly unaware of any serious problem of addiction, and state that there is no black market, with the possible exception that hemp and smoking opium may sometimes get past the customs authorities and into the waterfront district to Chinese and West Indian consumers. There are approximately 350 pharmacies in the city, less than a score of known addicts, and two doctors (out of a total of 40 in the United Kingdom) whose authority to prescribe drugs is currently under suspension. One of the two doctors has succeeded in curing himself of his addiction, and it is expected that his authority to prescribe drugs will be restored if he makes application. The officers reflected an attitude of great respect for the medical profession, and stated that they are "not encouraged" to approach the doctors in matters within their jurisdiction; if a questionable or unusual practice comes to their attention, they are expected to report through channels to the Home Office and the matter may then be taken up through the Ministry of Health and the local medical boards.

It was also stated that although the pharmacists are universally cooperative, some doctors, especially the older practitioners, would probably refuse to cooperate with the police concerning their patients under any circumstances, and the suspicion was voiced that "90% of the doctors up here don't keep any records at all." There was no identification between addicted persons and persons engaging in criminal activity.

In Edinburgh, with a population of half a million, two men are assigned to policing the Dangerous Drugs Act, and one investigation conducted by them within the last eighteen months has resulted in the preferring of charges. This was the case of an addict who had made application simultaneously to more than one doctor for care, with a long record of similar activities in the past. Because his wife cooperated with the police in reporting on his activities, he was let off without a sentence as a result of their recommendation to the prosecutor. The officers speculated that he might receive a short prison sentence if he were caught and charged again. They also recalled one case in the preceding year involving a doctor-addict who appeared to have violated the Act by making personal use of drugs purchased by him for administration to his patients. This case resulted in the conveyance of a warning to the doctor without the preferment of charges.

There are seven firms manufacturing narcotic drugs in Edinburgh, accounting for a substantial part of the industry in the United Kingdom. There has been one case of theft from one of these firms since World War II. The police cooperate informally with the firms in checking any applicant for employment about whom there may be suspicions (either of addiction or as a possible thief).

DENMARK

Narcotic addiction (aggravated by war-accumulated stocks of morphine) was recognized as a problem in the waterfront area of Copenhagen in the nineteen forties, but it is now believed to be largely confined to sailors off foreign ships. There have never been extensive smuggling operations, nor evidence of organized black market activities. Danish officials have found no apparent relation between addiction and criminality.

It is believed that there have been approximately a score of cases of addiction among Danish medical practitioners in the last decade. Addicts in prison populations are an insignificant proportion, less than one percent. Copenhagen has also been plagued with a mild outbreak of hemp (marihauna) smoking, centered along the waterfront and related to the recent upswing in juvenile delinquency in the same "tough" areas.

The Danish law regulates the importation, manufacture and distribution of drugs by a licensing and required-records system. Neither addiction nor possession is an offense *per se,* and most violations involve the forgery of prescriptions, punished by fines or very light prison sentences. Addicted persons may be hospitalized for voluntary detoxification, but they do not come into custody except by the commission of some ordinary criminal offense.

Following a governmental study in 1953-4, reportedly provoked by complaints about the loose practices of a few doctors in Copenhagen, the Danish statutes were revised[29] to give the Board of Public Health broad authority over the practices of physicians in the prescribing of euphoriants (including prescription for themselves). Prescription records are scrutinized by the Medical Officer of Health, and if a doctor violates the Medical Officer's rulings, or abuses his rights to prescribe, the latter right may be suspended, after notice and hearing, by the Board of Public

Health for a period of one to five years. Provision may be made for the issuance of prescriptions, on behalf of a suspended doctor to meet the needs of his practice, by a regional medical officer or by a colleague designated for the purpose. A doctor who violates a suspension order may be subjected to prosecution, fine and imprisonment. (The maximum penalty for any offense is two years' imprisonment.)

By the same enactments the Minister of Home Affairs and Housing was given broad authority to curb the importation and use of any drugs found by the Board of Health to be "highly dangerous by reason of their narcotic properties," and to make regulations to confine the use of such drugs to use for medical and scientific purposes only. Under this authority the prescribing of drugs for addicts has been centralized in the control of a special committee of doctors in Copenhagen, which passes upon each case of allegedly incurable addiction and prescribes or authorizes the prescription of proper stabilizing doses of drugs.

Officials with many years' experience disclaim any recollection that drug addiction has ever been a major problem in Denmark. The new law and regulations are recognized as a restrictive trend, but their aim is to tighten control over the practices of doctors, in professed emulation of the British system, rather than outright prohibition.

SWEDEN

The laws of Sweden,[30] last revised in 1933, impose controls on the import, manufacture, distribution and sale of nar-

cotic drugs, by means of licensing and reporting requirements under the jurisdiction of special administrative
units in the Royal Medical Board and the Division of
Pharmacies. Penalties of up to two years are provided but
in practice the courts give very light sentences, and offenses
are in the petty misdemeanor category (forging prescriptions, failure to keep records, etc.). The administration of
the laws and regulations is very loose and informal. There
are only two inspectors to cover the country (500 pharmacies; population, 7 million). Prescriptions are supposed
to be filed by the pharmacist and held for two years, but
no registers are kept and there is no supervision over medical practitioners except that incidentally given by the
chief medical officer of each of the twenty-five counties (a
doctor who has general responsibility for supervising the
providing of all medical services).

In Sweden the pharmacist (Apotek) is a professional
man of considerable standing, and such control as exists is
principally exercised through him. He is also a semi-official
functionary under the national health laws, with certain
duties as a civil servant. There are supposedly 500 to 600
addicted persons in the country, and according to a 1954
survey, approximately 20% of these are medical doctors.
In that year 130 addicted persons received treatment in
hospitals, and public health institutions.

In the official view, addiction in the ranks of the medical
profession itself is a serious problem. Doctors also sometimes become "easy prey," in prescribing freely and becoming, in effect, peddlers. When this is discovered
(through reports from the chemists or inspection of their
records) the Royal Medical Board sends for all prescrip-

tions issued by the doctor for analysis, interrogates him informally, and if he is found to be offending, may refer his case to the Board of Medical Discipline. If found guilty by the Board, the doctor may be warned, or sometimes his right to prescribe narcotics may be limited to the issuance of prescriptions to be filled by one or two chemists, or it may be cut off completely. For flagrant offenses the Board may suspend his medical license.

Doctors cannot dispense drugs directly to patients except in case of emergency, and seldom do so. They do not buy drugs from a wholesaler, but must file prescriptions with the chemist, showing whatever purchases they wish to make as destined for use in their own practice. Regulations fix maximum dosages which may be dispensed per one prescription, and the chemists are held strictly accountable for delivering any drug in violation of these prescription regulations.

A Swedish doctor may prescribe narcotics to a known addict in the course of a bona fide attempt to effect a cure, but ordinarily the doctors recommend hospitalization, and it is possible to commit an addict by medical order. There are no special institutions for treating addicts, but the facilities of Sweden's excellent mental hospitals are available for this purpose. Doctors are *not* permitted to prescribe stabilizing dosages for addicts, so that, besides the loose prescription practices of a number of doctors, there is considerable amount of dissembling by addicts, forging of prescriptions, etc. And there is believed to be a small black market in drugs. It is noteworthy that there is practically no diversion of drugs from the seven companies which manufacture them, or through the chemists (one offense in the latter category every two or three years).

Heroin has never posed a special problem, but Sweden imposed a ban upon it in 1952, and this has caused continuing dissatisfaction among some members of the profession. Some doctors assert, however, that heroin is much more dangerous in terms of addiction liability than the other opiates.

Outpatient treatment of addicts in the open departments of public health hospitals is not regarded as a success because, "the drug peddlers are right in the lounge waiting."

In sum, Sweden seems to illustrate the consequences of a policy which neither vigorously represses drug addiction nor yet seeks to alleviate it by vigorous health measures. The problem remains small-scale, but abuses and the illicit traffic have made their appearance.

NORWAY

The Norwegians are concerned about their drug addiction problem, with an estimated 700 addicts[31] (mostly concentrated in the Oslo area), in a population of 4 million. Controls have been very lax. Doctors may treat addicts, including the administration of stabilizing doses, but if they do so too freely the Ministry of Health may issue a warning or suspend the doctor's right to prescribe drugs. No doctors have ever been prosecuted for violating drug laws and regulations.

Although registration and licensing requirements are

provided, they have not yet been vigorously enforced. For example, unlimited "repeat" prescriptions were freely permitted until the adoption of a new regulation last year. Most addicts have met their needs by addressing themselves to one of twenty or thirty doctors (half of them in Oslo) who have acquired a reputation for prescribing drugs freely, and this situation has caused the Department of Health to press for new regulations which would create a control board similar to that established in Denmark.[32]

If a doctor wishes to reduce the dosages of a patient under his care (which happens in thirty or forty cases per year), he may notify the Health Department, which then puts out a bulletin on the case to pharmacists and other doctors, advising against the prescription of drugs to the individual patient involved. Local health authorities may initiate the same arrangement in the case of addicts who come to their notice, referring the case to a doctor to be handled in this fashion. Mental hospitals will accept patients for treatment on a voluntary basis, for periods up to nine months, but there is no provision for involuntary commitment for addiction alone.

The prescription records kept by pharmacists are supervised by two inspectors (who also have many other duties) and if a doctor's prescription practices appear to be far out of line, the Health Department may write to him or refer the matter to the medical officer of his district, though the Department had no power to impose penalties or enforce its views prior to the new regulations referred to above. It is emphasized that the police never take the initiative in connection with any narcotic drug matter, and that there are no officers specially assigned to this field. The law enforcement arm acts only upon the complaint of the Health Department.

There are a few cases of theft of drugs annually and many (several hundred) cases of forgery and fraud in connection with prescriptions. These offenses are not seriously regarded by the courts and the sentences given are light. Ten to fifteen doctors a year get into trouble with their medical boards for personal addiction (two such cases ended in suicide last year).

Health Department officials recount that publicity about the new regulations has provoked a number of visits and communications from addicted persons, who are leading normal lives and who are very much concerned that repressive policies would drive them into supporting an illicit market.

There is little relation between addiction and criminality; addicted persons are virtually unknown in Norway's penal institutions; and those who end in prison usually are there for repeated petty offenses, such as the forging of prescriptions.

BELGIUM

Belgian narcotics laws impose registration, license and record requirements on the narcotic traffic at all levels: import, manufacture, sale and distribution. Drugs may be dispensed only on prescription, and prescriptions must tally with the doctor's record book and inventory. Nine inspectors constantly check the records of Belgium's 4,000 pharmacies (in a population of 9 million).

Formerly, if it appeared from prescriptions that the doctor was prescribing drugs irresponsibly, the inspector could refer the matter directly to the Department of Justice, which might initiate a prosecution. This has been changed, and the new procedure is for complaints to be referred to a Commission Medical Provinciale. There are nine of these commissions, established on a regional basis, and each inspector (who is also a pharmacist), belongs to one commission. This change is for the protection of doctors, who used to be subjected to almost certain disgrace and ruin in their professions by being put on trial on complaint of the Justice Department regardless of the outcome.

Doctors are also subject to the jurisdiction of one of the provincial medical boards, semi-public bodies presided over by a judge, which have authority to censure them for misconduct or, in flagrant cases, to deprive them of their right to practice medicine. There have been few actions against medical practitioners under these provisions.

Addiction is not a crime *per se,* but addicts frequently commit petty crimes in connection with sustaining their addiction, so that they are liable to prosecution. The Justice Department uses this as a lever to compel submission for voluntary treatment (detoxification), which is provided in special sections of public mental health facilities. The number of persons in institutions for this purpose varies from ten to twenty-five.

There is probably some illicit trafficking. Convictions for forging prescriptions for narcotic drugs average ten per year. Addiction is almost always medically induced at the outset. In 1954 the pharmacy inspectors detected 203 new addicts in the course of checking prescription records (which is done periodically and does not cover all pharmacies every year); 8 doctors, 3 pharmacists, and 2 addicts were convicted of offenses involving prescriptions; sentences ranged from 15 days to 3 months (suspended in both addict cases), and fines from 500 to 2000 Belgian francs ($10 to $40).[33]

If a doctor has an addicted patient for whom therapy has failed, he may report the fact to the Commission Medical Provinciale and, with the Commission's approval, he may then proceed to set up a stabilizing regime. He is protected in this, since the local inspector is a member of the Commission. But the number of instances in which such arrangements have been made is trifling.

ITALY

Italian officials know of only a few hundred addicts, approximately fifty of whom are sent each year to public mental health institutions. It is estimated that in the life of the Italian narcotic drug laws, which have been in force for fifty years, approximately one hundred medical practitioners have been subjected to prosecution.

A recently enacted law[34] is considerably more severe, however, and the Ministry of Health is now policing the medical profession rigorously. Supervision is provided through a provincial health officer in each of the ninety-two provinces, but when an offense is suspected, the matter is promptly turned over to the police and the Justice Department for processing as a criminal case. A Central Narcotics Bureau has been established, and personnel is assigned to it from the national and local police arms. The new law prescribes mandatory minimum sentences in a comparatively harsh penalty structure.[35]

Pharmacists are rigidly controlled because of a strict limitation on the number of licenses (15,000 in the country), resulting in keen competition for the right to operate a pharmacy. Any deviation from the regulations as to the keeping of prescriptions and records, when discovered in the course of inspection by the regional health officer or the police, may result in loss of the pharmacy license.

Because of this strict hold on pharmacies, the pharmacist is used as an observer-informant, and if his suspicions are aroused he is expected to communicate promptly with provincial officers. Doctors are also under a direct obligation under the new law to denounce any known addict to the police,[36] and their rights to prescribe are limited to bona fide medical purposes which do *not* include prescriptions for addicts.

Although addicts may be incarcerated directly in a mental health institution by the police, to be held at the discretion of the hospital staff until it is determined whether they can be rehabilitated,[37] in practice the police often hold addicts in jail and put them through "cold turkey" withdrawal. The authorities also not infrequently succeed in prosecuting addicts on the basis of their presumed intent to sell illegally, from the fact of possession of large amounts of drugs.

There is a provision by which, after incarceration in a mental hospital and observation by a special medical commission, an addict may be determined to be incurable, in which event the medical commission may recommend that he be permitted a stabilizing regime. In practice, however, this provision is used only for addicts with medical complications.

The largest problem, in the official view, is the transit traffic in narcotic drugs being imported in raw form, and processed for trans-shipment to the United States black market. The special narcotic squads of metropolitan police departments are mostly concerned with this type of smuggling and clandestine manufacturing activity. There is also a considerable amount of forgery of prescriptions, theft of drug stocks, and similar crimes, indicating an unsatisfied demand for drugs.

ADDENDUM

Miscellaneous additional information acquired in the course of this study seems worthy of passing note. In Switzerland the basic law of 1924 was revised in 1951[38] to give the Federal Health Service comprehensive rule-making powers. But licensed physicians may acquire and dispense drugs without restriction, except for local regulations in a few cantons. Doctors may report addicts to the cantonal authorities if they believe the authorities should intervene to protect the interests of the addict's family or the community. There were 109 known addicts in Switzerland in 1954, and 8 offenses against the federal law, punished by fines of 100 to 500 francs and sentences of 1 to 6 months.[39] France, which provides compulsory treatment for delinquent addicts,[40] reported the detection of 129 addicts in 1953, and 93 in 1954.[41] West Germany reports

4,374 known addicts, including 618 doctors,[42] and has just adopted a new code, imposing rigid controls with severe penal sanctions.[43]

For many years the USSR disclaimed any drug problem in its reports to the U.N.: "The social evil of drug addiction has been eliminated in the USSR as a result of the fundamental economic and social reforms of 1917 and the continuing rise in the well-being of the workers." But in 1957 the Russian Health Ministry issued new regulations,[44] providing in part as follows:

"All medical and pharmaceutical establishments in the USSR shall report all drug addicts, when they first come to them for assistance, to the psychoneurological establishments (or dispensaries) in the patient's place of residence so that he may be registered and given the necessary treatment.

"All medical establishments and doctors shall avoid prescribing narcotic drugs for a patient, particularly over a long period except in cases of absolute necessity, bearing in mind that it is carelessness on the part of doctors which is almost the sole cause of drug addiction in the USSR.

"The vicious practice of giving drug addicts prescriptions enabling them to obtain drugs shall be prohibited."

Japan enacted a severe Narcotic Control Law in 1953[45] with graduated penalties of 5, 7 and 1-10 years for repeated offenses, including unauthorized possession. The law provides:

"No narcotic practitioner shall apply narcotics or supply same for application or prescribe narcotics for any purposes other than medical treatment.

"Despite the provisions in the preceding paragraph, no narcotic practitioners shall apply narcotics or supply same to other persons for application or prescribe narcotics for the purpose of easing the toxic symptoms of narcotic addicts or curing the toxication."

The Republic of China has experimented with total repression in its Order of 3 June, 1955,[46] involving the national emergency powers of the government "to thwart the policy of the communist regime of spreading the evils of narcotics." The Order required all addicts to present themselves to a court or police agency within one month, and to undertake to cure themselves (at their own expense, if medication or institutional care was required) within six months. Any addict succeeding in this undertaking "shall be exempt from punishment." For others, the punishment for being a drug user is 3-7 years' imprisonment (1-3 years for marihuana users), the same penalty is increased by two-thirds for a relapse, and for a third offense, the penalty is death. For the sale, transportation, manufacture or cultivation of poppies or opiates, the penalty is death (life imprisonment or death, at the court's discretion, if the offense involves marihuana). Other penalties include trafficking in poppy seeds, 7 years to life; dealing in the paraphernalia of addiction, 1 to 7 years; possession of drugs with intent to sell, 10 years to life; and possession of poppy seeds, not less than 5 years.

Anyone maintaining a place for the use of narcotic substances, for gain, is punishable by death or life imprisonment, and any government official or member of the armed forces committing any offense, or shielding a perpetrator of an offense, suffers the death penalty. The Regulations direct, "The suppression of narcotic drugs shall be completed within one year from the date of the promulgation of these Rules," call for the establishment of "a network of detection and intelligence services . . . by coordinating the work of all investigating agencies," and set up an elaborate system of rewards for informers and penalties for neglectful local officials.

REFERENCES

1. 38 Stat. 1912, T. S. No 612.

2. 26 Stat. 620, 1890.

3. L. N. T. S. No. 1845.

4. U. N., First Opium Conference Agreement, 1947 (pp. 5-14).

5. 48 Stat. 1543, T. S. No. 863.

6. U. N., Conference on the Suppression of Opium Smoking, 1947 pp. 3-15).

7. U. N. Conference on the Suppression of the Illicit Traffic in Danger-us Drugs, 1947.

8. 61 Stat. 2230, T. I. A. S. No. 1671.

9. 62 Stat. 1796, T. I. A. S. No. 1859.

10. U. N. Pub. S. No. 1953-xi.6.

11. See, e.g., S. Rep. No. 1440, 84th Cong., 2d Sess., 1956 (pp. 2-4), and the documentation offered on behalf of the United States to the United Nations Commission on Narcotic Drugs in May, 1955 (reproduced in Hearings on "Illicit Narcotics Traffic," Sen. Judiciary Committee, Subcommittee on Improvements in the Federal Criminal Code, June 2, 3 & 8, 1955, Exhibit 9, pp. 275-79).

12. See e.g., Anslinger & Tompkins, The Traffic in Narcotics, New York, 1953 (p. 290); Hearings, Sen. Judiciary Committee (see #11), Part 5, Sept. 20, 1955 (p. 1437).

13. Reproduced in Hearings on "Traffic in, and Control of, Narcotics, Barbiturates, and Amphetamines," House Ways and Means Committee, Nov. 7, 1955 (pp. 470-71).

14. The reference is to Dr. Alfred R. Lindesmith. See, e.g., Lindesmith, Opiate Addiction, Evanston, Ill., 1947; and "The British System of Narcotics Control," Law and Contemporary Problems, Vol. 22, No. 1, Winter, 1957 (pp. 138-154).

15. It is also conceded that some difficulties are being encountered with marihuana (which is not an addicting substance) in metropolitan areas and mostly among West Indian immigrants, and that there is still some opium-smoking among Chinese in the London and Liverpool dock areas. In 1956 there were 103 convictions in the courts of the United Kingdom for offenses involving marihuana, 12 for offenses involving opium, and 29 for offenses involving manufactured drugs (heroin, morphine, etc.). Of the latter, over half were "addicts who obtained drugs by forged prescriptions, or by getting supplies simultaneously from more than one doctor," and 8 were for failure to keep drugs in locked receptacles or to keep required records. "Report to the United Nations by H. M. Government . . . on the Working of International Treaties on Narcotic Drugs for 1956" (pp. 6-7).

16. Dangerous Drug Act, 1920, 10 & 11 Geo. 5, Ch. 46.

17. Supplementary legislation of major importance is contained in two enactments: the Pharmacy and Poisons Act, 1933, 23 & 24 Geo. 5, Ch. 25, and the Dangerous Drugs Act, 1951, 14 & 15 Geo. 6, Ch. 48.

18. Governed by interpretative regulations, currently Dangerous Drug Regulations, 1953, S. 1. 1953 No. 499, Reg. 17, as amended in minor respects by Dangerous Drugs Regulations, 1954, S. 1. 1954, No. 1047.

19. Initially the regulations provided for the disciplining of medical practitioners by a special tribunal of medical officers; this provision has never been invoked in the entire history of the Act, and in the 1953 revision of the regulations it was therefore deleted.

20. Scaled upwards from maxima of £500 and two years, for second offenders, in the 1920 Act, by the Act of 1951. On summary conviction (without indictment) the maxima are £250 and 12 months; and if the court is convinced that any breach of a regulation is through inadvertence, the offender shall be fined only, not more than £50.

21. Regulations, 1953, *supra*, Reg. 9.

22. Report to United Nations, etc., 1956. See #15, *supra*.

23. Currently set forth in Regulations, 1953, *supra*, as Reg. 4.

24. "The Duties of Doctors and Dentists under the Dangerous Drugs Act and Regulations," Home Office, DD 101 [6th edition], 1956, par. 7.

25. Report, Departmental Committee on Morphine and Heroin Addiction, Ministry of Health, 1926.

26. See #24, *supra*, Appendix IV (pp. 13-14).

27. See #15, *supra* (p. 4).

28. In the view of many therapists heroin has properties of unique value in treating certain conditions, especially in the respiratory tract.

29. Acts No. 168 and 169, 24 May 1955. An extensive collection of narcotic laws and regulations has been published, in English translation, by the Social and Economic Council of the United Nations. The Danish acts are identified in this series as E/NL/1956 (pp. 99 & 129). Reference to the U.N. source will be made wherever possible in citing foreign authorities in this paper.

30. No. 559, Laws of 1933.

31. U. N. Commission on Narcotic Drugs, Summary of Annual Reports of Governments, 1955. E/NR/1955 (p. 49).

32. Promulgated 27 Sept. 1957, and not yet implemented. The Danish pattern, which in turn derives from the British, will be closely followed.

33. See #31, supra (pp. 45-46).

34. Law No. 1041 of 22 Oct. 1954, E/NL/1954 (p. 144).

35. 3-8 years and 30,000-4,000,000 lira fine for major offenses, including possession in some circumstances.

36. The criminal penalty for failure so to report within two days is a 10,000 to 50,000 lira fine for the first offense and 1 year's imprisonment, with suspension of the right to practice for an equal period, for subsequent offenses.

37. The law provides: "Art. 21. Any person who, by reason of serious mental deterioration caused by the habitual improper use of narcotic drugs, endangers himself or others or causes a public scandal may, at the request of the public security authorities or other interested party and after receipt of a medical report, be ordered by a magistrate to be removed to a clinic, curative establishment or mental hospital for detoxification treatment."

38. Law of 3 Oct. 1951, E/NL/1952 (p. 33).

39. See #31, supra, 1954 (p. 31).

40. Act of 24 Dec. 1953, E/NL/1954 (p. 1).

41. See #31, supra, 1953 (p. 19); 1954 (p. 32).

42. See #31, supra, 1953 (p. 20).

43. E/NL/1957 (pp. 57-84).

44. Order of 6 April 1957, E/NL/1957 (p. 61).

45. Law No. 14, 1953, E/NL/1954 (pp. 145-52).

46. Implemented by Regulations, 29 July 1955, E/NL/1956 (pp. 86-88).

FINAL REPORT

of the Joint Committee of the
American Bar Association and the
American Medical Association
on Narcotic Drugs

FINAL REPORT

RECOMMENDATION

The joint committee recommends to the House of Delegates of the American Bar Association and the House of Delegates of the American Medical Association that its activities as a special committee be terminated; and that the study of the narcotic drug traffic and related problems, initiated by it, be carried forward cooperatively through appropriate instrumentalities and research facilities within the permanent structures of the two associations.

REPORT

In this report the Joint American Bar Association–American Medical Association Committee on Narcotic Drugs is completing its original assignment as set forth in the A.B.A. House of Delegates resolution of February 22, 1955, "To explore with the American Medical Association the possibilities of a jointly conducted study of the narcotic drug traffic and related problems. . . ."* Its principal conclusions are two: that present methods of dealing with narcotic addiction and narcotic addicts raise questions which are urgently in need of study; and that the legal and medical professions, equally concerned, can most fruitfully pursue the subject in close cooperation through their respective associations. In passing, it is noted with great satisfaction that the joint committee's two years' work has been, in view of all concerned, a rewarding and eminently successful experiment in inter-professional cooperation.

The joint committee offers its observations and tentative conclusions here, and recommends its own dissolution, because it has reached a point where it believes the full resources of its parent associations must be called into play. The research it deems necessary seems too extensive to be undertaken by a temporary committee—when both associations support permanently organized research foundations precisely designed for such projects; and the policy determinations which must ultimately be made lie within the jurisdiction of permanently constituted divisions within both parent bodies.

With the aid of a grant from the Russell Sage Foundation, the joint committee has completed a factual analysis of present policies and present knowledge concerning narcotic addiction and the control of narcotic drugs, which was submitted with its interim report to the A.M.A. and

* 80 A.B.A. Rep. 408 (1955).

A.B.A. House of Delegates last year. This interim report, with its appendices, contains information concerning the medical, social and legal problems confronted in dealing with drugs and drug addiction in the light of existing policies and available knowledge. It does not attempt to provide solutions, but does reflect a degree of dissatisfaction within the legal and medical professions concerning current policies which tend to emphasize repression and prohibition to the exclusion of other possible methods of dealing with addicts and the drug traffic.

The interim report recommends additional research in five major areas:

1. An experimental facility for the outpatient treatment of drug addicts, to explore the possibilities of dealing with at least some types of addicted persons in the community rather than in institutions.

2. An extensive study of relapse and causative factors in drug addiction.

3. The development of sound and authoritative techniques and programs for the prevention of drug addiction.

4. A critical evaluation of present legislation on narcotic drugs and drug addiction.

5. A study and analysis of the administration of present narcotic laws.

The joint committee urges that the above projects and studies be carried on under the auspices of its parent associations, in order to provide additional experience and data needed to appraise alternative methods of controlling narcotic addiction and dealing with the drug addict.

In making these recommendations, the joint committee

is aware that they may encounter opposition from those who tend to view the drug problem as essentially a problem of criminal law enforcement, and specifically that the United States Narcotics Bureau has indicated that it will oppose them. The joint committee regrets this attitude demonstrated by the Narcotics Bureau. In the committee's opinion, the Narcotics Bureau, together with all other persons and agencies interested in the problem, should welcome research in the areas which have been indicated. The narcotics problem is too important to be insulated from intensive study and investigation.

While zealous law-enforcement efforts have unquestionably played a part in reducing drug addiction—and will indisputedly continue to be required in curbing the illicit drug traffic—experience has not demonstrated that the laws and enforcement policies urged by the United States Narcotics Bureau provide the full answer to the problem. On the contrary, experience suggests that further investigation of the problem is essential. The joint committee trusts that nothing will be permitted to hamper inquiries which may lead to fruitful results, and which should, at the very least, provide a factual basis for appraising alternative approaches to the problem.

On the basis of its studies and deliberations, the joint committee has reached the following conclusions concerning narcotic addiction and methods of dealing with narcotic addicts, which it submits for the purpose of indicating the need for further studies along the lines recommended above, and with the hope that these conclusions, although subject to reappraisal in the light of additional data, will be serviceable guides:

1. There appears to have been a considerable increase in drug addiction in the United States immediately following World War II; the increase was most apparent in the slum areas of large metropolitan centers and especially among minority groups in the population.

2. As a result, the federal government and many states passed legislation imposing increasingly severe penalties upon violators of the drug laws, as a means of dealing with the apparent increase in addiction.

3. This penal legislation subjects both the drug peddler and his victim, the addict, to long prison sentences, often imposed by mandatory statutory requirements without benefit of the probation and parole opportunities afforded other prisoners.

4. Though drug peddling is acknowledged to be a vicious and predatory crime, a grave question remains whether severe jail and prison sentences are the most rational way of dealing with narcotic addicts. And the unusual statutory basis of present drug-law enforcement, substantial federal domination in a local police-power field established by means of an excise measure enforced by a federal fiscal agency, invites critical scrutiny.

5. The narcotic drug addict because of his physical and psychological dependence on drugs and because of his frequently abnormal personality patterns should be as much a subject of concern to medicine and public health as to those having to do with law enforcement. But the ordinary doctor is not presently well equipped to deal with the problems of the narcotic addict, and even his authority to do so is in doubt.

6. The role of medicine and public health in dealing

with drug addiction and the drug addict should be clarified. There must be a new determination of the limits of good medical practice in the treatment of drug addiction, and an objective inquiry into the question whether existing enforcement policies, practices and attitudes, as well as existing laws, have unduly or improperly interfered with good medical practice in this area. As part of this evaluation, consideration should also be given to the possibility of helping both the addict and persons formerly addicted through open clinic facilities as well as in closed institutions such as Lexington and Fort Worth.

7. It can be stated emphatically that no acceptable evidence whatsoever points to the indiscriminate distribution of narcotic drugs as a method of handling the problem of addiction. On the contrary, the use of such drugs, except for legitimate medical needs, should be discouraged by the best available means. Individuals who have become addicted should be given the benefit of all known medical and paramedical procedures to encourage them to withdraw from dependence on narcotic drugs voluntarily; those who have withdrawn should be given psychiatric and social-agency help as long as necessary to assure against relapse. We need much more information than is presently available about the best means of handling addicts who, despite the best professional efforts, continue to be dependent on drugs. An experiment conducted by experts (as proposed above in this report) should be charged with getting information on this point.

8. There is a high rate of relapse on the part of addicts who have been in the care of narcotics hospitals and installations for the treatment of addiction. The real reasons

for this must be determined. Factors to be considered include the physical and personality make-up of the individual, the social pressures applied to him, both adverse and constructive, and the attitude and sophistication of medicine and the law regarding addicts and addiction.

9. Some responsible authorities state that the physical and psychological dependence of addicts on narcotic drugs, the compulsion to obtain them, and the high price of the drugs in the illicit market are predominantly responsible for the crimes committed by addicts. Others claim that the drug itself is responsible for criminal behavior. The weight of evidence is so heavily in favor of the former point of view that the question can hardly be called a controversial one. But this point is so fundamental to the development of a sound philosophy of management of the problem that any residue of reasonable doubt must be resolved. In this connection the joint committee deplores the hysteria which sometimes dominates the approach to drug addiction problems by persons in positions of public trust. In terms of numbers afflicted, and in ill effects on others in the community, drug addiction is a problem of far less magnitude than alcoholism. Crimes of violence are rarely, and sexual crimes are almost never, committed by addicts. In most instances the addicts' sins are those of omission rather than commission; they are ineffective people, individuals whose great desire is to withdraw from the world and its troubles into a land of dreams.

10. It appears that neither compulsory hospitalization of all addicts nor permanent isolation is practicable at the present time. Hospital facilities to deal with narcotic addicts are not adequate in numbers, staff or program, and

the permanent isolation of addicts, even if feasible, would not be a solution but only a temporizing maneuver—the very antithesis of the medical and scientific approach to the physical and behavioral problems of man.

The foregoing recommendation and report will be submitted to the House of Delegates of the American Medical Association with resolutions similar to those appended hereto, merely conformed to adapt the language of the resolutions to A.M.A. purposes. The object of the resolutions is to continue cooperation between the two associations in further mutual efforts along the lines suggested in this report and the joint committee's interim report.

It is firmly believed by the joint committee that the work it has already done clearly indicates a need for further joint efforts, carried on by both associations through permanent instrumentalities which have greater continuity, more facilities, and a broader mandate than the joint committee. Accordingly, favorable action on this report and its appended resolutions is respectfully urged.

For the American Medical Association:
C. JOSEPH STETLER
R. H. FELIX, M.D.
ISAAC STARR, M.D.

For the American Bar Association:
RUFUS KING, *Chairman*
EDWARD J. DIMOCK
ABE FORTAS

Summary and Recommendations of

REPORT ON NARCOTIC ADDICTION

by the Council on Mental Health
of the American Medical Association
(1956)

Summary and Recommendations of Report on Narcotic Addiction by the Council on Mental Health of the American Medical Association (1956)

SUMMARY

1. Study of the operations of clinics which dispensed drugs to addicts between 1919-1923 shows that data available on these clinics are not sufficiently objective to be of any value. The clinics were set up hastily as emergency measures, did not have well defined objectives, were inadequately staffed, and made little effort to rehabilitate addicts. There is no doubt that there was some abuse of the clinics, but the extent of the abuse is undeterminable.

2. The medical profession played a major role in formulating a policy which led to closing the clinics.

3. The best evidence indicates that the incidence of addiction in the United States has declined since passage

of the Federal Narcotic Laws. During World War II the number of addicts reached an all time low, probably because of the decline in illicit traffic due to war-time conditions. The incidence of addiction has risen, as would be expected, since the end of World War II. There are probably not more than 60,000 addicts in the United States at present.

4. Addiction in persons under 21 years has also increased since World War II. The extent of adolescent addiction, however, does not justify the degree of public alarm which has risen. Adolescent addiction is not a new phenomenon.

5. The greatest incidence of addiction occurs in minority groups residing in the slums of certain large cities. Such areas have the highest rates of delinquency, alcoholism, crime, and mental disease, as well as of addiction.

6. Deliberate proselyting by drug peddlers in order to expand their market plays only a minor role in spreading addiction; rather, addiction spreads from person to person. Initial doses are usually supplied to the neophyte by a friend, and as a friendly gesture.

7. The most common psychiatric entities associated with addiction are personality disturbances and character disorders.

8. Opiates do not directly incite persons to commit violent crimes. Crimes committed by addicts are usually crimes against property. A proportion of addicts—various sources give figures ranging from 25 to 80%—have records of delinquent activity prior to addiction.

9. Current treatment of addiction is unsatisfactory. The relapse rate, though not known exactly, is high. One pos-

sible reason for such poor results is lack of facilities for post-institutional treatment.

10. The advisability of establishing clinics or some equivalent system to dispense opiates to addicts cannot be settled on the basis of objective facts. Any position taken is necessarily based in part on opinion, and opinions on this question are divided.

RECOMMENDATIONS

1. *Improvement of the care of addicts.* It is recommended that the American Medical Association continue to study and to support reasonable proposals designed to improve the treatment and prevention of drug addiction. Such measures might include:

(a) Development of institutional care programs in cities and states with significant problems.

(b) Study of various means to obtain institutional care in states with small addiction loads. One such proposal is for several states to set up an institution which would be operated jointly.

(c) Development of programs for intensive post-institutional treatment of addicts. Such measures would include supplying of various social services, vocational rehabilitation and, where possible, psychotherapy to addicts for adequate periods following discharge from institutions. In many instances, available facilities in other programs might be utilized. States with serious problems should develop special programs for addiction.

(d) Development of methods for commitment of addicts to institutions by civil action rather than through actions in the criminal courts. In this connection the Council further recommends that where civil commitment procedures can be used criminal sentences for addicts who are guilty only of illegally possessing and obtaining opiates, marihuana, and cocaine should be abolished. Criminal sentences for illegal sale of narcotics should be retained but persons who are addicts and who are sentenced for such offenses should have the same opportunity for probation and parole as is afforded offenders against other laws. Mandatory minimum sentences for addict violators would interfere with the possible treatment and rehabilitation of addicts and therefore should be abolished.

(e) The Council strongly recommends that the policy of voluntary admissions for the treatment of addiction should be continued, extended and encouraged.

(f) Continue support and expansion of mental health programs. Because of the importance of psychiatric factors in addiction, such programs should eventually have an effect in reducing addiction even though not specifically aimed at that problem.

2. *It is recommended that the American Medical Association support proposals for increased research* on the problems of addiction. One of the current difficulties in formulating adequate programs is lack of knowledge which can be gained only through research. Support should be given not only to "basic" laboratory investigations but also to continuation of sociological studies, and to an intensive program of clinical research based on adequate facilities

for following addicts after institutional discharge. Such research might yield results that would be valuable in areas other than addiction.

3. *Clinic Plans.* In view of all of the available evidence at the present time it does not seem feasible to recommend the establishment of clinics for the supply of drugs to addicts. This is true for the Eggston resolution and the plan of the New York Academy of Medicine even though there are many aspects of these plans that could be looked upon with favor. This opinion should be subject to frequent review in accordance with new scientific knowledge that may become available.

4. *It is recommended that the American Medical Association continue to study* the narcotic laws with the view of further clarification of the rights and duties of physicians and allied professional persons in the handling of addicts. The phrases in the current law ". . . in the course of professional practice only" and "prescription," remain vague and confusing, despite Supreme Court decisions. Regulations on dispensing drugs to addicts should be eased so that the patients can have a reasonable time to arrange their affairs prior to entering a hospital for treatment. The 1924 Resolution of the House of Delegates should be revised. Consideration should be given to broadening the Resolution to include a plan endorsing regulations somewhat similar to those currently in force in England.